Praise for Marcy McKay

Amazon #1 Hot New Release!

"I read this book all in one sitting. Informative ... funny. I loved this, and think you will, too."

Melissa Hallmark Kerr, PhD, co-founder of Brain Savvy

"Marcy has gracefully personalized and documented the importance in taking care of the mind-body connection, as well as how our life's experience plays into stress, trauma and anxiety."

Erin K. Bishop, MA, A Breath of Wellness

"Transforming Your Stress is current and useful as we navigate our new normal. A great resource and an easy read."

**Terry Bentley Hill, attorney and founder,
#StopMindingYourOwnBusiness**

"Already dog-eared ... what a beautiful piece of writing."

Adam Jones, author of Rose Bowl Dreams: A Memoir of Faith, Family and Football

"Marcy hits the nail on the head. Every. Single. Time. Run, don't walk, to grab *Transforming Your Stress*. I bought a copy for all my closest friends and family."

Bobbye Marrs, author of *I Am My Beloved's*

"*Marcy McKay gives it to you straight. She offers actionable items and solutions.*"

Robert, a reader from Australia

"*I've loved all of Marcy's McKay's novels. Now, I love her nonfiction, too. You feel like you're sitting in a coffee shop with her, and she's explaining your life to you.*"

Tonja, a superfan

"*Transforming Your Stress* is fun, entertaining, and helpful. Thanks you for this user-friendly sensation."

Sam Ferris, a neuroscience geek

Transforming Your Stress (When Life Feels Like a House Fire)

Aug. 25, 2022

Enjoy!

Mary Uhely

When Life Feels Like a
House Fire

TRANSFORMING
YOUR
STRESS

MARCY M. MCKAY
BESTSELLING AUTHOR

First edition: October 2020.

Book design by Get Covers.com
Graphic Designs by Rae McCollum. Instagram: @byrae.ai.
Author photo by Katie Billstrom, Doubletake Photography.

Ebook: 978-1-950637-88-1
Paperback: 978-1-950637-63-8
Published by SkipJack Publishing, LLC.
www.skipjackpublishing.com

To my father, Roy Mason

*Who taught me to whistle
louder than anyone I know*

And so, she burned. Burned to the ground.

Though pain, time and courage, she began to rise.

Rising from the ashes. Shining brighter than ever before.

Marcy McKay

Contents

Part III. THE SCIENCE BEHIND YOUR STRESS

Part IV. YOUR STRESS BLUEPRINT

Also by Marcy McKay

FICTION:

Pennies from Burger Heaven

Bones and Lies Between Us

Stars Among the Dead

The Moon Rises at Dawn

Disclaimer

A note to the reader:

Transforming Your Stress is for informational purposes only. It cannot guarantee results.

Please consult your doctor or mental-health practitioner before making any changes to your medical protocols or lifestyle.

Foreword

Before you start reading, please know my Book Accelerator course, *Transform Your Stress*, is available online to enhance your learning. It has all the book's exercises and assessments together in one workbook, as well as 3.5 hours worth of bonus video content:

https://marcymckay.teachable.com/p/transform-your-stress/

Also, I do not have a financial interest in any of my recommendations in this book, so my suggestions are not influenced by advertisers. Additionally, I continue to grow and change as a person, so I reserve the right to change my mind about any topic in the book.

Introduction

I was home alone when IT happened. The kind of "it," where there's a clear "before" and "after," so your life changes forever. My husband was at work that afternoon. Our daughter was already back at college and our son had just started his senior year in high school. He'd be gone to college this time next August, so the clock was ticking to make the most of every moment. We'd be empty nesters soon.

I sat at my desk staring at my blank computer screen with wet hair, bare feet, jeans and a long sleeve t-shirt. My debut novel had been released two years earlier and had won some awards, but I was struggling with the sequel. I had placed my fingers on the keyboard for the thousandth time – when our smoke alarm screeched a high-pitched warning.

My heart pounded at being startled but I didn't sense danger because I didn't smell smoke. I nervously tiptoed through our one-story house, while the alarm kept screaming.

Nothing was wrong in the dining room.

The living room was fine, too, so why was I shaking?

I continued to look around. There was no smoke or flames.

Nothing.

All three bedrooms were clear. The alarm shrieked on, so I phoned my husband and shouted over the noise, "Should I call 911?"

"Yes!" he hollered.

We hung up, but I didn't make the call (insert *knife-in-the-heart* guilt #3,942).

I stepped into the den. Nick the pug typically dozed nonstop on the couch. Instead, he stood on the sofa with his fur raised, looking bug-eyed toward our backyard.

"What's wrong?" I asked him.

No answer. A shiver ran up my spine. I wanted to check on our other dog. Nick followed me through the kitchen, then into the backyard.

Our yellow Labrador Retriever, Gypsy, was racing laps around the lawn. That typically didn't concern me since she'd always been high energy, but something about her frantic vibe frightened me.

"What's wrong?" I asked the same question, then turned to find the answer.

Smoke rose like ghosts along the entire roofline from my house.

Not the chimney.

The roof.

I can still picture the gray wisps rising up to the cotton-candy clouds in that bright blue sky.

I whipped out my phone and called 911 at 3:57 p.m. on Friday, August 25, 2017, in Amarillo, Texas.

That's when my old life ended.

A Different Conversation

I know you're tired of hearing about COVID-19, but it's been a hot topic since March 2020: best practices to combat the disease, the climbing number of those who've tested positive, as well as the ever-growing fatality rate that's passed 700,000 deaths in the United States and over 5,000,000,000 worldwide at the latest update of this book.[1]

The heroes on the front line.

The economy.

Jobs.

It's devastating.

The sad-and-all-too-familiar political finger-pointing that's driven a deeper wedge between us. This deadly disease has spotlighted even more the disparity between the haves and the have-nots.

The hoarding.

The hate.

The lack.

The rage.

It's heartbreaking to think about the millions of people with no food, no jobs, no money to pay the bills, sky-rocketing unemployment, not to mention the abuse and addiction escalating behind closed doors.

If that's not upsetting enough, add a divisive presidential election in the U.S., the systemic racism which could not be ignored anymore following the death of George Floyd and others, then the civil unrest that followed across the globe.

Regardless of your opinions on all of the above, we seem to have forgotten the Golden Rule: *Do unto others as you would have them do unto you.*

If the least among us shows who we really are, then we aren't doing so well. If you're financially able, please donate to the many worthy causes to improve the disaster in whatever areas speak to you. Buy gift certificates from your local businesses. Help a neighbor in need.

Kindness matters.

It's always mattered, but now – our future literally depends on it.

All of the above is real and vital, but they are not the purpose of this book. I want to talk about your stress, your anxiety, your overwhelm[2], your mental exhaustion because those matter, too.

Why?

Because they have specific messages for you. They've been trying to get your attention for a long time, but you didn't know how to decode the information and follow-through with action.

That's what I didn't understand after our fire. A crisis magnifies who we are – good and bad. We're feeling that right now on every level.

As individuals.

As families.

As organizations.

As countries.

That's our painful reality these days. Life can be tough. We must slow down and reevaluate, separately and collectively. *The Washington Post* reported after just three months of isolation and soaring unemployment during 2020 that 30% of all Americans are said to be suffering with symptoms of anxiety or depression.[3]

That's not exactly a bombshell revelation.

Dictionary.com defines stress as, "A state of mental or emotional strain or tension resulting from adverse or very demanding circumstances."

Anxiety is defined as, "A feeling of worry, nervousness, unease, typically about an imminent event or something with an uncertain outcome."

Yep, we're all in the right place. This book uses the term "stress" as mental or emotional strain due to the pandemic or other demanding circumstances, rather than medically-diagnosed anxiety.

However, if you do have such a diagnosis, you are not alone. The Anxiety and Depression Association of America states that anxiety disorders are the most common mental illness in the United States, affecting 40 million adults, 18 years or older, or 18.1% of the population every year. Plus, women are twice as likely to be affected with Generalized Anxiety Disorder than men.[4]

I personally do not like the term "mental" illness because it has such a negative connotation.

Ugh, he's so mental.

But the Powers That Be did not ask my opinion. Your stress symptoms are absolutely connected to how you're handling life these days, but they're also related to the past.

Your past.

Everyone has faced their own house fire of some sort: death, divorce, debt, a diagnosis. Drama comes in all shapes and sizes.

That's why you're struggling now. You don't just have the past to contend with, but you're also worried about you, your family and friends now, your sliver of the world, and what the "new normal" will look like.

There's so much more to it.

I'm Not a Doctor and I Don't Play One on TV

I realize that one woman's house fire does not remotely compare to the global destruction of a pandemic, but trauma isn't a contest. Pain is pain. Stress is stress. Besides, we all use our own experiences to make sense of reality. That's human nature.

Turns out, all my challenges were a great crash course for surviving quarantine life. I recognize the same struggles, extreme emotions, and patterns that my husband and I faced back in 2017 are happening to so many today.

As difficult as our fire was, the battles my family experienced over the 10 months that followed were even worse because everything that could go wrong actually did. I'll spare you the details, but let's just say – they sucked.

Sometimes, Mark and I just had to laugh to keep from crying. We'd collapse into bed each night, yet still wake up exhausted. Regular tasks seemed so much harder, from making coffee to sitting down and drafting emails for work. Foggy brain, loss of time, the inability to concentrate, all the stress eating. We both seemed constantly on edge.

That's what is happening to you these days and why I wrote this book. I wish something like this had existed for me back then to explain my stress and anxieties. Better yet, to show me how to make it better.

I graduated from Baylor University in 1988 with a Bachelor of Arts in Public Relations and a minor in Spanish. That means I can put a positive spin on anything which has come in handy during Armageddon. Plus, I can speak enough Español to have a meaningful conversation with any Spanish-speaking toddler.

I'm not a licensed therapist. I'm not a medical doctor, researcher, or a social worker of any kind. I do not claim to be an expert in the realm of mental health. I'm just a gal whose life fell apart after a house fire, so she went on a journey to Humpty-Dumpty herself back together again.

Once I found the answers I'd spent my whole life searching for, I kept wondering, *"WTH! Why has Oprah not told me this? Why are we not teaching this to all our children this second?!"*

I found some answers from "this expert," then more from "that guru," and put it all together to save you the time and trouble. Some will disregard anything I have to say because I do not have letters behind my name, which I find fascinating. I've also never been to culinary school, yet I've cooked for my family for over 30 years.

Does that make the food less real? I make a mean Eggs Benedict.

Check out the resource guide in the back if you want to read more from the actual experts. Even after (or while) reading this book, some should still consider working with a therapist, psychologist, life coach, psychiatrist, or other mental health practitioner. I know I am.

You might also need to go to a medical doctor or other healthcare provider, yet, *Transforming Your Stress* can still help you. You have to understand what the problem is in order to solve it, and your struggles may not be what you think.

Objectives:

In telling you my personal story, I hope *Transforming Your Stress* will:

1. Guide you in making peace with your own stress patterns: physically, emotionally and behaviorally.
2. Show you the basic science behind your anxieties, so you understand what has kept you stuck or unable to change in the past. Good news, it's not your fault!
3. Help you create a personal Stress Less Action Plan with downloadable worksheets, assignments and exercises throughout the book. Just because the world seems like it's falling apart doesn't mean you have to.

Better. Faster. Stronger.

Since 1996, businesses and not-for-profit boards have hired me to facilitate their strategic planning sessions, staff trainings and team-building exercises for their employees. I've also worked one-on-one with individuals. We didn't call it coaching back then. We called it helping people. I've always been interested in being the best version of myself, then guiding others to do the same.

Better. Faster. Stronger.

The Six Million Dollar Marcy!

Kudos if you're old enough to get that joke. For almost 25 years I've noticed patterns among my clients. The perfectionists, the procrastinators, the people-pleasers, the bullies and the bulldozers. The backdrop of the institution didn't matter because people are still people.

Some are incredible.

Some are total jack-wagons.

Most of us are somewhere in between. We all have a light side and a dark side.

I never understood why some folks *got it* and made the changes they needed to make, while others didn't. Not that they wouldn't. It's like they *couldn't*.

It was as if there were an invisible wall stopping them from making the very changes they wanted in their lives. There was a missing link somewhere I didn't discover until years later after my own life fell apart.

That could be what's happening to you now.

Notes

1. Johns Hopkins University & Medicine. (2020). COVID-19 Map. Johns Hopkins Coronavirus Resource Center. https://coronavirus.jhu.edu/map.html.

2. "Overwhelm" has been a noun since at least 1596, according to the Oxford English Dictionary. The definition given, "[t]he action of overwhelming; the fact or state of being overwhelmed; an instance of this," is the way it is still being used today. Even so, no other major dictionary includes the noun.

3. Fowers, A., & Wan, W. (2020, May 26). A third of Americans now show signs of clinical anxiety or depression, Census Bureau finds amid coronavirus pandemic. The Washington Post. https://www.washingtonpost.com/health/2020/05/26/americans-with-depression-anxiety-pandemic.

4. Facts & Statistics. Anxiety and Depression Association of America, ADAA. https://adaa.org/about-adaa/press-room/facts-statistics.

Rules for the Road

To make the most of our journey together, here are a few ~~demands~~ friendly suggestions:

Read the Book in Order

Transforming Your Stress is foundational. One concept builds on the other. I understand if you want to skip ahead to the magical chapter you think has all the answers, but stress is a complex subject. We'll start with simpler side of complicated, then work our way out together. There are important insights each page, so please slow your roll and read the book from start to finish.

Do This!

In reading about your stress, you might experience some anxiety because we're not running from ourselves anymore. We're going to talk about the stuff we don't typically share with others. Topics we might not like to even think about – but then again that is part of the problem.

Throughout the book I have exercises for you to complete. I call them – **Do This!** (how original). These responses are for your eyes only, so please try to be as candid as you can, even if that's not easy.

I don't need to write anything down, Marcy. It's all in my head.

Really? This already?

Fine. Our lives look different on paper. You cannot see the patterns of your life. You cannot connect the dots to your coping strategies of **today** to your stressors from the **past** if you do not have the information laid out before you.

Like it says – **Do This!**

Some people want to read the book from cover to cover as fast as they can, then go back and complete all the **Do This!** exercises. Others want to read the chapters and complete everything as they move along.

Do what feels right for you.

Tools You'll Need:

1. **A notebook or notepad and a pen** – To take notes, to complete the various *Do This!* assignments, or to jot down insights you have along the way. If you'd rather use your computer – go for it. Just record your thoughts and information in the same spot to keep track of everything.
2. **Open mind** – Question anything you want, but at least be willing to consider other perspectives.
3. **Honesty** – It does yourself no good if you lie to yourself about your stress. Be as upfront as you can to pinpoint your challenges and where you need to change.
4. **Compassion** – I find so many of us are too hard on ourselves. Kindness is a much more effective tool for change than criticism, even if that's a new concept for you.

This Process Is NOT One Size Fits All

Sigh. I wish this was *fix your stress in three easy-peazy steps!*, but that's not how life works. Reality looks more like:

The car wreck.

Losing your wallet.

Too many bills and not enough money.

Realizing your teen has an eating disorder.

Your marriage implodes after 20 years.

Procrastinating on telling your elderly parent he needs to stop driving.

If you read something that does not apply to you just file the information away because it might help someone else you know. It's hard to understand the full impact of your stress. You think it's just one area of your life, but it turns out – it's several, different parts that are interconnected. Plus, we're exploring sensitive subjects. Curiosity and compassion are essential. I'll be with you every step of the way.

I Like to Laugh

I'm not minimizing anyone's pain or making fun of you in any way. Humor is a great tool and a wonderful way to lift your spirits. The Mayo Clinic says laughter has many medical benefits. It cools down your stress response, as well as decreases your heart rate and blood pressure. In the long term, laughter improves your overall immune system.[1]

Mark and I have ended many days since 2020 watching silly sitcoms or fun romcoms. We laugh, unwind, and reconnect with each other. That energy boost gives us the oomph to keep going during these extreme times, which *ain't* easy because stress is is no laughing matter.

Notes

1. Mayo Foundation for Medical Education and Research. (2019, April 5). Stress relief from laughter? It's no joke. Mayo Clinic. https://www.mayoclinic.org/healthy-lifestyle/stress-management/in-depth/stress-relief/art-20044456

PART I
YOUR STRESS

1. Your Stress is 100% Real

It took two-minutes-and-thirteen seconds from the time our fire alarm first went off until I phoned 911 from our backyard.

Two-minutes-and-thirteen seconds to turn my family's world upside down.

The emergency woman was so calm as I ushered the dogs into the house and hollered our information over the alarm. I had just passed through the kitchen a minute before, but now giant flames shot at me through the ceiling vent above the stove.

I screamed and ducked, the heat brushing my face. The room was spinning. The dogs almost tripped me they were so frightened. There were more flames. I struggled to catch my breath. The alarm kept shrieking, while sirens wailed in the distance.

The emergency operator reminded me she was there. I do not remember what she said. I just clung to her voice and kept moving.

The doorbell rang – it was a policeman.

I gave him the dogs then dashed back to grab my family's fireproof safety deposit box with all our birth certificates, passports and other important documents. I also took my laptop since it's my anchor as a writer.

Even now, the memory feels like someone else walking through my dreams.

Outside, five fire trucks and a police car stood in front of my home. Both sides of the block were barricaded. Irrationally, I hoped our neighbors wouldn't be mad.

It was so hot. Chaos swirled as I stood by my favorite oak tree, regretting all I'd left behind: my shoes, my purse, photo albums, baby books, the Christmas stockings I needlepointed for the kids when they were little.

There were still no major flames (apparently, they stayed contained in the attic), but my stomach turned queasier. The same eerie smoke kept rising from the roofline, while I repeated to myself like a mantra: *It's fine, it's just smoke, it's fine ...*

Ignorance is bliss because I had no idea that smoke does as much damage as a blaze. The fire marshal said if they'd waited even five more minutes to go inside, our house would've been a total loss.

Every time I read that sentence I still feel ill. At some point I called to update my husband, but he'd already sensed something was wrong and was driving home.

We never spent another night in that house.

I worry that inside – you're falling apart, too.

Danger, Will Robinson! Danger!

Coronavirus, global pandemic, self-isolation, quarantine, shelter-in-place, COVID-19, masks, lockdown, vaccines, antidotes, positive cases, recovered patients, death toll.

The vocabulary alone is terrifying, but this isn't some bizarre sci-fi movie or your overactive imagination.

This is our current state of affairs. I realize you might be all modern with your almond-milk cappuccinos and whatnot, but to your subconscious mind – these are still cavemen times.

Truly. It thinks we're all dressed like the Flintstones, gathered together in our tribes to battle saber-toothed tigers to stay alive. Our survival brains scan for danger (real or perceived) 24/7.[1]

That's its only job. Our modern-day tigers have become waking up to an overflowing email box, demanding jobs, plus, dealing with ups and downs of life.

Reality check. COVID-19 more than meets all the requirements of danger:

It's an invisible threat.

Is this pandemic even real or a political hoax?

We don't know who is infected and who is not.

We can't agree if masks help or hinder infection.

Communities were forced to shut down.

Having to shelter-in-place cut us off from friends, family, a regular routine and income.

We're hardwired for community, so isolation is difficult, if not torturous.

No country seemed properly prepared for this crisis, so what hope does that give to regular folks like you and me?

The world is struggling with how or when to reopen.

How will the economy recover?

We don't know how long it will take to rebuild.

What will "normal" look like?

Do vaccinations help or hurt?

When will this all end?

None of the above even includes the bigger conversational time bombs like politics and social justice issues that some don't want to discuss one bit, while others can't seem to talk about anything else. Social media has turned into a battleground.

All this ramps up your stress.

Depression is the leading cause of disability worldwide.[2]

It's not your imagination.

This is serious business.

Science of the Brain

I first learned about neuroscience in 2011 through a program called EBT (Emotional Brain Training) by Dr. Laurel Mellin, *New York Times* bestselling author of *The Pathway – Follow the Road to Health and Happiness*. According to her website, stress is the #1 underlying cause of up to 90% of health problems.[3]

45% of Americans have at least one chronic disease.

Nearly 10% of the United States population has diabetes, and 35% of all adults have metabolic syndrome (a combination of obesity, high-blood pressure, Type 2 diabetes and poor lipid profiles).

Mental illness and substance abuse affect 20% of Americans and death by suicide has increased by about 30% since 1999.

America ranks *last* in life expectancy among the 12 wealthiest industrialized nations, even though the U.S. spends double per person on healthcare than all the other countries, including per-capita pharmaceutical expense.

Those statistics are just for the United States alone.

They're also terrifying.

Make no mistake, life since March 2020 has been a traumatic experience for millions of people across the globe. In talking about your stress, we'll discuss the good, the bad and the ugly. Especially, those dark places hurting inside you right now.

Don't worry. We all have them. Turns out, your anxiety serves an important purpose and it's not to wreak havoc on your life.

Notes

1. Cacioppo, J. T., Cacioppo, S., & Gollan, J. K. (2014, June 27). The negativity bias: Conceptualization, quantification, and individual differences: Behavioral and Brain Sciences. Cambridge Core. https://www.cambridge.org/core/journals/behavioral-and-brain-sciences/article/negativity-bias-conceptualization-quantification-and-individual-

differences/3EB6EF536DB5B7CF34508F8979F3210E.

2. Facts & Statistics. Anxiety and Depression Association of America, ADAA. https://adaa.org/about-adaa/press-room/facts-statistics.

3. Mellin, L. Emotional Brain Training. https://www.ebtconnect.net/science.

2. It's "Not that Bad"

It's "~~Not~~ that Bad"

The firemen ripped out every ceiling of each room of my family's ranch-style house to stop the flames. Between the smoke and water damage, the entire place was ruined, but they were able to save the majority of our belongings.

We were beyond lucky and I still feel grateful. You may think your "home" is the roof over your head, but it's your dishes, your favorite holiday decorations, your most comfy pj's that you slip on before bed each night. Even more than the stuff – it's the memories your family created together.

That's what makes a house a home.

The smoke-and-water damage was so severe it took months to repair, but we absolutely could have moved back. People who drove down our street just thought we'd emptied the place for a massive remodel.

It's "not that bad," well-meaning folks told me.

They're right in that it wasn't a towering inferno. My home didn't burn to the ground. The dogs and I made it out alive. The hair singed off part of my face, but it grew right back.

To this day, some people act like I'm a total Drama Queen about the entire situation.

How many times have you told yourself, "It's not that bad."

Or, "It's fine."

Maybe you're saying that to yourself these days. Red flag those phrases in your mind.

"It's not that bad," or "It's fine," equal emotional wounds. You're trying to normalize your pain. That tactic rarely works. It can actually intensify the anguish because you're minimizing your feelings. Just because you can't see something doesn't make it less real. Invisible wounds hurt even worse when you do not acknowledge them yourself.

How many of you have felt guilty since March 2020? *It's not that bad, it's fine, so many others have it so much worse.*

Yes, they do, and ...

Your pain still matters.

Since our fire wasn't "that bad," I felt guilty for being such a wreck. But a switch flipped inside me that day.

Immediately, I went from happy to miserable.

I felt anxious all the time, and not my "normal anxious." This feeling was supersized.

My sleep, which was already problematic, became non-existent. I'd also been battling my hormones and serious weight gain in my fifties – the scale showed I weighed more than I did with either of my pregnancies. I'd already seen multiple doctors, but could not find anyone to help.

All of the above worsened after the crisis and I became depressed. I couldn't seem to crawl my way back to happy. I didn't feel like me anymore.

My regular coping strategies stopped working. Namely,

slapping on a smile as Susie Sunshine, the childhood role I played growing up. Because therapy had saved me during my twenties, I tried a highly-recommended family counselor. She was nice, but just tried to sell me an expensive marriage retreat.

So I tried another.

Nothing.

I attended church more and made yoga a priority. Hell, I even drank kale juice.

I needed more than a spiritual pep talk or veggies in a glass because something was *wrong* with me, physically, emotionally, behaviorally and psychologically.

I couldn't seem to figure out why or how to feel better.

The 2020 Rollercoaster

The world shared in a collective grief while quarantining. Trapped at home and trapped in our hearts. Even as some communities have reopened, we're still facing an enormous crisis together that seems to have cracked us open wide. Many are still struggling.

Here's what I heard from family, friends and clients. Do you recognize yourself in any of these descriptions during an extended crisis?

I feel like I'm holding my breath.

I feel like I'm walking through molasses.

I feel trapped on a rollercoaster and can't step off.

Everything feels out of sync.

I feel like I'm drowning beneath the overwhelm.

I feel like this is some bizarre sci-fi movie that keeps getting stranger.

I can't get a 'handle' on my emotions.

I can't focus. It's exhausting.

I want to stay in bed, cry and stress-eat/overdrink/binge-watch TV, etc.

So many others have it so much worse than me. I feel guilty complaining at all, but ...

I'm struggling so much more than anyone knows.

I'm not sure how much longer I can take this.

Life feels unsettled and weird.

I worry I'm losing my mind.

Whether you worked full-time from your kitchen table, and/or home-schooled your kids full-time, too – there just weren't enough hours to get everything done each day. Managing your *To Do* list was a joke. Plus, everyone's emotions are so messy! You became sick of each other and maybe bickered non-stop.

At first, during the lockdown, you gave up and let the kids do pretty much whatever they wanted, as long as they didn't destroy the place. Many days, you each hid in different rooms to avoid a complete free-for-all.

Maybe your entire family was not home during the pandemic, so you'd sometimes lie awake at night, worrying about their safety.

You might live alone. You didn't hug anyone for months and the loneliness really wore you down. You tried to stay positive, but it was difficult with all the gloomy news.

Or, you're SICK OF ALL THIS! You're so over this #$%@ pandemic!

It's not your imagination.

This *is* difficult.

Illustration 1

<u>A FEW 20202 EMOTIONS</u>

Shock. Fear. Sadness. Anger. Despair. Frustration. Relief. Numbness. Impatience. Overwhelm. Depression. Strength. Uncertainty. Guilt. Peace. Hostility. Happiness. Betrayal. Uselessness. Anxiety. Denial. Confusion. Helplessness. Contentment. Disbelief. Avoidance. Irritation. Agitation. Loneliness. Stress. Gratitude. Shame. Powerlessness. Irritation. Apathy. Isolation. Thankfulness.

I don't know about you, but I can cycle through *all* these feelings within any given week. My husband would probably say I do so within the hour.

Everyone is different. What worries me might not affect you one bit. That doesn't make one of us wrong. It just means we do not share the same stressors. Remember this process isn't one-size-fits-all.

Healing is not linear. It happens cyclically. We often circle back to the same core issues to understand them on a new and deeper level with new dimensions added to it.

Plus, some stress *is* beneficial. Good stress helps you meet deadlines, stops you from stepping onto the elevator with that homicidal-looking maniac. For me that looks like exercise, watching an intense movie, writing this book for you.

Mixed Feelings

As if life isn't challenging enough, there's also the added turmoil surrounding the disease (stay home or attend that cool pool party?). All amidst a global recession, high unemployment, a divisive presidential election and political unrest over systemic racism, classism, sexism and pretty much every other *ism* out there.

Not to mention our 24/7 lifestyles, where it's difficult to find any balance. Your inner world seems to match that instability, giving you so many conflicting emotions. For example:

You might feel grateful you and your family are safe, but also guilty for such a selfish thought since so many are at-risk, sick, or have died.

You may feel stressed and lonely working full-time from home, but also a little relieved to be away from certain co-workers.

Perhaps you feel grateful your kids are home from college, but also tired of constantly ordering more groceries.

THIS emotion, but also THAT one, too.

Maybe you've been surprised by the unexpected blessings along the way:

You do not miss that impossibly long commute to the office.

Your young children love Game Night every evening after dinner so much that they refused to give up that family time even after the world began to reopen.

To maintain your sanity, you started jogging again and have already lost 15 pounds.

Forced time at home has helped clarify what you value most.

Brené Brown said, "One piece that contributes to feeling weary in this pandemic is the energy it takes to hold space for many competing emotions. I think we're all juggling lots of mixed feelings."[1]

You're up. You're down. You're all over the place. Each week seems to present new challenges as the world desperately tries to flatten the curve, all while maneuvering so many other explosive topics online.

It's. All. Too. Much.

Yet, here we are.

Do This!

List a few of your competing emotions. If need be, refer back to the Emotions table (Illustration 1). Feel free to include other emotions not listed there.

For example, what worries you right now? What are you grateful for these days?

I feel _____ , but also _____.

I feel _____ , but also _____.

I feel _____ , but also _____.

Notes

1. Ayers, A. (2020, May 19). Brené Brown talks virtual commencement speech, choosing courage over comfort. The Daily Texan. https://thedailytexan.com/2020/05/19/bren%C3%A9-brown-talks-virtual-commencement-speech-choosing-courage-over-comfort.

3. Let's Rip Off the Band-aid

Our fire was deemed an accident. The 1950s ceiling vent above the stove had been running (that's where flames shot at me) and faulty wiring in the attic started the blaze. The firemen worked hard to contain all the damage inside the house.

I have a new home, a new life – Mark and I are much happier as a couple than before our fire, but you know what?

I still miss our old house. We lived there for 17 years. Our kids were three years old and four weeks old when we first moved in. I miss Pizza Family Movie Nights every Friday as a young family, pumpkin-carving parties and dying Easter-eggs together. Mark and I fought, cried, laughed and loved in our home.

The house survived the fire, but the new owners (who are great) tore it down the day after they took ownership. It's now a beautiful lot full of green grass until they decide what's next for them. It took almost a full year before I could even drive by because I felt so sad, as if our time there was somehow erased or diminished. That empty lot matched the hole in my heart.

Intellectually, I know it's not true, but our pain is often irrational and quite real. That adds to our stress.

Your Pre-Apocalypse Life

Whatever you thought 2020 would look like, I'm assuming COVID-19 was not it. Whatever had you hoped, dreamed and planned for – that life is gone.

As in, gone forever.

Take that in for a moment.

You might feel that truth deep in your bones, while others will think it's total BS.

For the doubters: even if *you* feel completely unscathed by the pandemic, the majority of the world has drastically changed around you. That, in and of itself, impacts you.

Besides, if we were to play a little game I call, *Let's Be Honest*, your world wasn't perfect before. No matter how shiny your Facebook page is, there are certain aspects you probably wanted to change. Maybe you'd even tried, like your:

Perfectionism.

People-pleasing.

Procrastination.

Anxiety.

Overwhelm.

Insomnia.

Stress-eating.

Overdrinking.

Overspending.

Always starting and stopping projects.

Inability to focus.

Not stepping into your true purpose for this world.

Never feeling good enough.

Feeling you're too much or a burden.

Unworthiness.

Self-harm.

Always being 'the fixer.'

Over-giving without getting enough (if anything) back.

I get it. Your secrets are safe with me.

Do This!

What do you miss about what passed as "normal" for you? I understand this might make you sad, angry or frustrated to think about, but those unrecognized emotions are adding to your stress now. You need to acknowledge your feelings.

Do this however you prefer. Write deep, wearing-your-feelings-on-your-sleeve grief (like me) … *OMG! I miss hanging out at the coffee shop. I miss my friends. I miss hugging people. I miss sitting in church on Sunday mornings. I'm so sad …*

Or, make a laundry list of emotions – 1, 2, 3.

There's no right or wrong here.

Just do it.

_____

_____

_____

_____

_____

_____

_____

Who is Your Why?

This work can feel rocky at times. It's three steps forward and two steps back. Who are you willing to face challenging times for and to change for in your life overall? Who inspires you to be a better person?

Who is your why?

My "who" are my children. Yes, I love my husband, but our daughter and son bring out something deep and primal inside. They are part of me. I would move heaven and earth for my babies. And not in a creepy, helicopter mom sort of way – just pure love.

So much of adulting is doing stuff you do not want to do. Calling the airline about your destroyed luggage. Fixing your cracked windshield. Setting a boundary and voicing a need.

If you want to do this work for yourself alone, fantastic. Claim it. Maybe you want to change for your community or the greater good.

Outstanding. I struggle to change for myself, but always will for my kids because they are the next generation for our family. I want to give them my best, so they can do the same for my (future) grandbabies.

If you can't think of anyone right now to be your *why*, what about a pet, or a historical figure? Maybe a favorite character from a book or movie?

Fill in the blank, them keep them in mind as you move forward. We're about to dip in deep into your stress.

Do This!

Who inspires you to examine your stress and find healthier behaviors?

_____

Why is he, she or they so important or special to you?

_____

_____

_____

Who is your WHY?

_____

What would their life look if you changed?

_____

_____

_____

_____

_____

_____

_____

How would your life be different if you changed?

_____

_____

_____

_____

_____

_____

PART II
YOUR STRESS PATTERNS

4. Stress Origins

Back when I was young enough to think the built-in sharpener of my box of crayons was the *coolest* thing ever – I also carried a secret. I *had to* shut my closet door each night before going to bed. This was a standard ritual I did to stop the monsters from grabbing me in m y sleep. I'm not sure why shutting the door assured my safety because let's face it – if monsters had really been there, they could've just turned the knob to slink out and kidnap me anyway.

However, part of my fears was based on reality, and not just from watching too much Scooby-Doo. When I was about seven years old, I woke up one Halloween morning to ghosts hovering above me in my canopy bed (yes, I was totally *that girl* with a canopy bed. Do not shame me. I'm trying to help you).

I shrieked, then blinked several more times to realize they were actually tiny Kleenex ghosts dangling from the canopy. My ten-year-old brother rushed in laughing, thrilled that his prank had worked. He had made what seemed like a million ghosts, but was probably a dozen tissue-goblins he had tied with long strings, then hid above my bed until showtime.

It was clever and maybe someday I'll forgive him.

Still, second-grade me was terrified.

That's the deal with fear. Most parts are not real. We worry about so many things that never happen, but often there *is* a kernel of truth lodged somewhere in our subconscious, even if it's not a direct correlation. There were never any monsters in my closets or boogeymen under my bed ... until that *one time* there was.

There was still more to my constant anxiety.

I want you to think more about your past. Memories may pop up that you hadn't thought about in years, or old hurts you'd rather stay forgotten. Do your best to sit with that discomfort because it's important information.

This is one of my favorite chapters because it shows *where* your anxieties started. It was a major "aha!" moment for me, with multiple lightbulbs flashing through my mind as I watched Mastin Kipp's online Masterclass nineteen months after our fire. He showed how my past coping strategies kept me from moving forward and had the research to prove it. All my responses to our house fire suddenly made sense.

More importantly, I now understood everyone, too: me, my mom and dad, my kids, my husband and his parents, all the generations before us – the Masons and the McKays. Former clients who couldn't change. Friends, enemies ... the whole #$%@ world! It both enlightened me, and gave me so much compassion for everybody's shortcomings. I felt like I had the secret decoder ring to finally understanding the universe.

I want to share some of the successes of my clients throughout the book. All their names have been changed to protect their privacy. Results are also anecdotal.

Meet Nicole

Nicole is a smart, forty-something with a heart of gold. She's enjoyed a long, successful career in the corporate world and has been happily married for years. However, beneath her winning façade, she privately suffered shamed and battled standing up to a few overbearing coworkers at the office.

She was probably in fifth grade in her tiny hometown when she noticed her friends took vacations and bought back-to-school clothes, while hers rarely went anywhere. Plus, she and her brother always wore hand-me-downs.

Nicole also began to understand her mother struggled a lot, and remembers the time the local police brought her mom home after finding her huddled on the railroad tracks. Or, when Nicole and her dad spent hours trying to coax her mom out from under the bed. By high school, Nicole realized that despite being from a family of four, she was really on her own.

A few of Nicole's stress origins included:

Poverty.

Her mom's undiagnosed mental illness.

Emotionally-unavailable mom.

Inconsistent father.

Rules always changing at home.

Chaotic childhood.

Forced to be the parent to her mom.

Loneliness.

Neglect.

We focused on Nicole's self-worth, hypervigilance and constant people-pleasing, zeroing in on the dynamics with her coworkers. I'll share more of her story later, but once Nicole changed, she said, "I no longer feel broken."

This is Not the Blame Game

You've relied on your old patterns because they worked, even if you don't like them or they wreak havoc in your life. Whether it's over-drinking, mismanaging money, your constant self-doubt, or going along to get along with others.

One big caveat before we begin. We're about to step into tender territory. Some of your stressors started in childhood, while others formed during your adult years. Regardless of when and where they began, many bring up what I call the 3 P's:

Personal.

Painful.

Private.

I am not blaming your mom or dad, or whoever raised you for what they did or did not do while you were growing up. Maybe it was that mean teacher in third grade or a coach who humiliated you in high school. We just want to pinpoint where your stress started, so you can create healthier habits.

We're all products of our past. It's what makes us who we are today – the good, the bad and the ugly. Everyone knows how difficult adulting is, so I'm not disrespecting anyone.

Do This!

Take the Stress Origins Assessment[1] on the next page to begin uncovering the root cause of your anxieties.

Remember, my Book Accelerator course, *Transform Your Stress*, has all the book's exercises and assessments together in one workbook, as well as 3.5 hours worth of bonus video content:

https://marcymckay.teachable.com/p/transform-your-stress/.

STRESS ORIGINS ASSESSMENT
Circle all that you've experienced during your lifetime.

1. Rules always changing at home.
2. Raised by a single parent.
3. Parents divorced during childhood.
4. Family moved around a lot.
5. Chaotic childhood.
6. Parent(s) unavailable (emotionally or physically).
7. Passive/aggressiveness at home.
8. You had to parent your mom or dad.
9. Expected to be seen and not heard.
10. Expected to be not seen or heard.
11. Foster care.
12. Parents argued, but with no resolution.
13. Parents never argued, but you sensed their tension.
14. Fear used to control you.
15. Alcohol/Addiction.
16. Feelings minimized as a child: "Don't feel that way." "Big boys don't cry."
17. Taught to people please.
18. Experienced bullying.
19. Felt unloved or unwanted as a child.
20. Near-death experience.
21. Cheating or betrayal.
22. Money wounds.
23. Narcissistic parent or sibling.
24. Physical/emotional disability in fam.
25. Death in your family.
26. Religious wounds.
27. Gaslighting (psychological manipulation).
28. Stalking.
29. Humiliation.
30. Loneliness.
31. Didn't feel *at home* in your home.
32. Black sheep of the family.
33. Told you were too much/drama queen.
34. Played a role growing up: hero child/black sheep/mediator.
35. Sexual orientation wounds.
36. Boss from hell.
37. Poverty.
38. Hunger.
39. Homelessness.
40. Racism.
41. War and violence.
42. Theft, vandalism, other crimes.
43. Accident or natural disaster.
44. Generational family trauma.
45. Birthing trauma.
46. Adoption.
47. Medical procedures.
48. Emotional abuse.
49. Physical abuse.
50. Sexual abuse.
51. Body issues.
52. Trauma of any kind.

Marcy's Stress Origins

My father stood at six feet, three inches and weighed over

three hundred pounds. He smoked Camel cigarettes, no filters. He was larger than life to me and my friends. We all loved and feared him.

Roy Mason had a big laugh. Big love. Big anger. My parents told me every day they loved me, and I felt their love. My dad was also a nickname kind of guy. He called me – Mouse, my brother Greg was Turkey and our younger sister Molly was Little Molly Sunshine.

However, our dad's feelings also ran hot or cold. We never knew who would walk through the door when he came home from work.

Fun, let's go get ice cream dad?

Moody, brush by us, then go sulk in his room dad?

Walk in yelling at us for no reason dad?

Emotionally, he could leave us wounded and unsure. My mom is a strong, kind woman and I can recall loud arguments between them when she verbally pushed back. It got ugly.

I'm a "nice girl" from a "nice family," yet here are some of my stress origins from adulthood:

Natural disaster (fire).

My husband and I triggered each other with our unresolved wounds.

Death in the family (I was 20 when my dad died).

Don't forget my childhood stressors:

Rules always changing at home.

Chaotic childhood (even if it was loving).

My brother, sister and I had to parent our dad.

We were expected to be seen and not heard.

Feelings like sadness and fear weren't allowed because they were considered weak.

Always told I was a Drama Queen.

My dad was passive-aggressive with massive unhealed trauma.

There's much more to it, but you understand. Let me be clear, I *loved* my father. I dedicated this book to him and am so grateful how he always encouraged me to step out in ways I would not have done without his support. He constantly reminded me that I was a leader and pushed me to be more. He also gave me my love of storytelling.

My father both empowered me and did some unintentional damage to our family, which is why I'm committed to changing these patterns so my kids don't inherit that same dysfunction.

I want you to move beyond your current struggles, too.

My Dad's Stress Origins

My father was in my life from 1966 until 1987 when he died. Roy Mason didn't do wimpy things like *feel his feelings*. Instead, he picked himself up by the bootstraps by overeating, chain-smoking and yelling. He drank alcohol, but I only saw him drunk once. That didn't bother me because I was 20 and too busy underage drinking myself at the same wedding reception.

Here are a few of his stress origins I've pieced together:

Rules always changing at home.

Parents divorced (my dad was 20, but I think it still hurt him).

Chaotic childhood (my grandmother was so loving, but ...)

Alcoholic father (my grandfather was a World War II veteran).

Physical abuse (from his father).

Fear used to control him.

Death in the family (my dad had a younger brother who died as an infant).

Humiliation.

Near-death experience (that story is forthcoming).

Body issues (severely overweight).

Life is not easy. Families are a curious mixture of love and hate. However, once you understand your stress origins more, you can create healthier patterns for a brighter future. Great job. Let's keep going.

Notes

1. Kipp, M. (2019-2020). Adapted from ProsperX program. personal communication.

5. Do Not Get Hung Up on Words

I only saw my dad's dad once during the mid-1970s, when I was seven or eight. The man showed up drunk on my family's doorstep from out of town to borrow money. I clung to my father's side as he introduced me to this stranger who was supposed to be our kin.

I mumbled a bashful hello, then ducked behind my dad. Apparently, my grandfather came home from World War II quite damaged and years later, left my incredible grandmother to marry his pregnant secretary.

My brother and sister recall different aspects of that day, but what we all agree that we'd *never* seen our father act like that before. He wasn't rude or disrespectful in any way, he just wasn't himself.

Even as young as we were, we all sensed:

THIS. IS. A. BIG DEAL.

The family reunion didn't last long after the cash exchange. I remember Dad telling Mom, "I'll never see him again."

My father spent the rest of the day in their bedroom.

I spent that afternoon deciding what I'd call that man the next time he came to visit us. I'd be ready. Not Granddaddy, that's what I already called my mom's dad. Poppy? Gramps? Papa?

Nothing sounded right.

I got hung up on words.

Didn't matter. We never saw him again.

Neither did my father. Years later in high school, Dad came home from work and mentioned in passing that his father had died days before, but he chose to skip the funeral. I asked him why he didn't go, but he just shrugged and walked away.

Once again, he spent the rest of the day behind closed doors.

Trauma

Swiss psychiatrist, Bessel van der Kolk, M.D., author of *The Body Keeps the Score (Brain, Mind and Body in the Healing of Trauma)* says, "One does not have to be a combat soldier, or visit a refugee camp in Syria or the Congo to encounter trauma. Trauma happens to us, our friends, our families, our neighbors. Research by the Centers for Disease Control and Prevention has shown that one in five Americans was sexually molested as a child; one in four was beaten by a parent to the point of a mark left on their body; one in three couples engage in physical violence. A quarter of us grew up with alcoholic relatives, and one out of eight witnessed their mother being beaten or hit."[1]

Those are alarming statistics and definitely not the most widely discussed topics.

Van der Kolk also explains parts of the brain that have evolved to monitor for danger remain overactivated after trauma. Even the slightest sign of danger, real or perceived, can trigger acute stress responses, coupled with intense emotional responses.

That's our caveman or survival brain I mentioned earlier.

Everyone Has Trauma

I bristled the first time I heard eons ago the speaker at a women's retreat say we all have trauma. I thought to myself, *uhhhh, no I don't. No trauma here.*

I mistakenly believed like so many others that trauma is a one-time event: a car wreck, physical abuse, rape.

Yes, and ...

Physical abuse, sexual abuse and emotional abuse absolutely constitute trauma, but so does everything on the Stress Origins Assessment (Chapter 4).

Were you lonely as a child?

Did your family move a lot?

Were you made to feel like your emotions were somehow too much?

That constitutes trauma, too.

I realize the tendency is to treat some items as more serious than others, but the stress all depends on how your body and brain absorbed the moment or events. As I said before, what is stressful to me might not bother you at all. It's a spectrum.

Do not get hung up on the wording:

Emotional wounds.

Emotional blocks.

Childhood issues.

Stress.

Family-of-origin issues.

Unresolved trauma.

Everyone has trauma, whether you grew up in a mansion or in a dumpster.

Those stressors become emotional blocks that stay lodged inside your body, which you feel physically, emotionally, behaviorally and psychologically.[2] You'll understand more as we keep going.

Whatever did or did not happen to you, your brain deemed those experiences as stressful or UNSAFE. It saw them as that saber-toothed tiger, so it set up coping strategies to help you manage. Maybe the threat was real, or it might have just been your perception, which still makes it real.

These patterns make perfect sense if we were to rewind the clock back to those anxious times. Whether it was a boss from hell five years ago, that abusive boyfriend from college, or your loving, but dysfunctional family.

For others, it means surviving horrible, unspeakable abuse.

Your past was painful. You're struggling in the present. Focus on healing now, so your future feels brighter.

That's how you change the pattern.

I think of trauma as emotional blocks. Colorful, wooden shapes like you played with as a kid. When stacked together, these blocks form our thoughts, beliefs and behaviors. Some are healthy, while others keep causing you to struggle, even if it's not a direct correlation.

I'd never experienced a house fire before, so where did my patterns begin?

This is your first global pandemic, so you cannot rely on that plague back in kindergarten. Instead, your guilt might stem from always playing mom as a child to your depressed mother. You might subconsciously feel responsible for the world's pain now. Maybe your parents divorced when you were quite young and feel that same loneliness all over again.

Stressors

We're all juggling with a lot of mixed feelings right now. You also have hurts stacked on tops of hurts inside you.

You may have long since forgotten or ignored what happened, but your body remembers everything. Those inner emotional blocks act like a wall of pain. Even if you're from a "nice family," and already understand your past: your bipolar father, your sibling with a physical-or-emotional disability, your childhood OCD.

Hurts stacked on top of hurts.

Your past trauma could be what's causing you trouble today – keeping you anxious, stuck and unable to move forward.

We'll examine this more.

Do This!

Which experiences on the Stress Origins Assessment (Chapter 4) have impacted you the most, and why?

This question is crucial. Even if it's difficult to write about, do your best to not hold back because it's zeroing in on important aspects of your patterns.

_____

_____

_____

_____

_____

_____

_____

Notes

1. A., V. der K. B. (2015). The body keeps the score: brain, mind, and body in the healing of trauma. Penguin Books.
2. Harvard Health Publishing. (2020, July 6). Understanding the stress response. Harvard Health. https://www.health.harvard.edu/staying-healthy/understanding-the-stress-response.

6. Let's Get Physical

Although I was fortunate enough to make it out of our house fire without a single scrape or burn, I woke up sore enough the next day that my whole body felt like I'd been beaten black and blue. Every inch of me ached and the fire alarm kept ringing in my head. I couldn't shut it off.

I didn't realize that my long battle with PTSD had begun. My insides screamed like Macaulay Culkin in *Home Alone* after he figured out he'd been left, well – home alone. AHHHHHHHHHHHHHHHHHHHHHHHHHHH!!!!!!!!!!!!!!

I call that my 911 feeling.

I *hate* that feeling.

I bet you've experienced it before, too.

My #1 place to carry stress has always been in my neck and shoulders. The depth of my tension equals my anxiety level. Both definitely got worse after the fire and flared up again early on in the pandemic to the point I could barely turn my head when I woke up.

That's understandable since I spent most days in front of a computer, either writing or on Zoom calls with clients. Still, a friend once teased me that I seem to carry the weight of the world on my shoulders.

She's not wrong.

After I began dealing with my stress origins, my PTSD, low-grade depression and other health problems suddenly made perfect sense. I began to understand that trauma changes you from the inside out.

The key to change is time, patience and practice with the right support. Because of this, I've learned to rewire my brain to create healthier patterns.

That's what I want for you, too.

Rachel's Story

Rachel first came to me when she was in her mid-fifties as the executive director for a well-known nonprofit in her community. She was also on five different high-blood pressure medications, antidepressants, and more. Even though she was a star student and athlete growing up, her home life had been quite the opposite. She endured a narcissistic mother who never physically abused Rachel or her younger siblings, but the emotional mistreatment and neglect were shocking.

A few years after college, Rachel fled an abusive marriage with her two young children in tow with nothing but the clothes on their backs. She returned distraught to her childhood home where her mother's narcissism began again, except Rachel set a major boundary this time. Refusing to tolerate any more unacceptable behavior.

She was banished overnight from her family. None of her brothers and sisters have spoken to her in decades, while her dad sneaks phone calls to her a few times a year.

Even though Rachel knew she had done the right thing, she still felt heartbroken. By the time I began working with her, she'd raised two incredible kids who were happily married with children of their own, Rachel was now married to a kind man, who was slipping into dementia, so she felt that familiar loneliness all over again.

Rachel had been to therapy years before, so she understood her mother's narcissism, but didn't realize the impact that her childhood still played in her adult life. That unworthiness felt buried deep inside her and unending.

In an effort to change, Rachel attended her first yoga class in 2019. She also spent a weekend alone in the mountains on a mini-retreat, and began asking for more of what she needed at home.

Six weeks after her first session, she got off two of her high blood pressure medications and had cut the third prescription's dosage in half. Rachel saw the physical-and-emotional benefits of dealing with the root causes behind her stress. That motivated her to keep going.

Before you make any changes to your medical protocols or lifestyle, consult your medical doctor or health practitioner. Prescriptions save lives.

Where Does It Hurt?

The fallout since 2020 has impacted millions. How many times have you thought with each new catastrophe, *I cannot believe this is happening?*

Trauma changes you from the inside out.

As we've already discussed, stress stays stored in the body until it's released. Where and how is your anxiety showing up for you these days? Even if you had those physical ailments before, take note because those are important details for you.

Your body is the physical entity of how you move and exist through this world. Whether you are short or tall, big or small, your body has experienced every second of life with you. It's seen a lot of action. Those specific aches and pains are more than a mere nuisance, they're vital to understanding your stress.

Peter Levine, PhD is the founder of Somatic Experiencing Training Institute in Boulder, Colorado, which specializes in "somatic experiencing."

"Somatic" means "in the body," as in moving that stress from your body.

Dr. Levine is also the author of *Waking the Tiger*. He says, "Trauma is perhaps the most avoided, ignored, belittled, denied, misunderstood, and untreated cause of human suffering."[1]

Your physical pain is so much more than just aches and ailments. It's the embodiment of your trauma.

Do This!

Please take the Physical Stress Assessment on the next page to start pinpointing your anxieties.

Check out my Book Accelerator course, *Transform Your Stress*, to enhance your learning. It has all the book's exercises and assessments together in one workbook, as well as 3.5 hours worth of bonus video content:

https://marcymckay.teachable.com/p/transform-your-stress/.

PHYSICAL STRESS ASSESSMENT

Please rate each symptom on a scale 1-5 as it applies to you today:

	Never	Rarely	Somewhat	Often	Always
Headaches	1	2	3	4	5
Migraines	1	2	3	4	5
Insomnia	1	2	3	4	5
Sleeping too much	1	2	3	4	5
Low energy	1	2	3	4	5
Brain fog	1	2	3	4	5
Fatigue	1	2	3	4	5
Anxiety	1	2	3	4	5
Depression	1	2	3	4	5
Vision problems	1	2	3	4	5
Ringing in ears	1	2	3	4	5
Tightness in neck	1	2	3	4	5
Tense shoulders	1	2	3	4	5
Dry mouth	1	2	3	4	5
Difficulty swallowing	1	2	3	4	5
Clenched jaw/grinding teeth	1	2	3	4	5
Shortness of breath	1	2	3	4	5
Tightness in your throat	1	2	3	4	5
Back pain	1	2	3	4	5
Nervousness/shaking	1	2	3	4	5
Cold hands or feet	1	2	3	4	5
Sweaty hands or feet	1	2	3	4	5
Chest pains	1	2	3	4	5
Heartburn	1	2	3	4	5

Rapid heartbeat	1	2	3	4	5
Churning stomach	1	2	3	4	5
Loss of appetite	1	2	3	4	5
Never full	1	2	3	4	5
Nausea	1	2	3	4	5
Diarrhea	1	2	3	4	5
Constipation	1	2	3	4	5
Numbness	1	2	3	4	5
Tightness in your hips	1	2	3	4	5
Tingling limbs	1	2	3	4	5
Aches, pains, tense muscles	1	2	3	4	5
High/low blood pressure	1	2	3	4	5
High/low blood sugar	1	2	3	4	5
Frequent colds/infections	1	2	3	4	5
Loss of sexual desire	1	2	3	4	5
Decreased sexual ability	1	2	3	4	5
Bloating	1	2	3	4	5
Weight gain	1	2	3	4	5
Weight loss	1	2	3	4	5
Hormonal imbalance	1	2	3	4	5
Autoimmune conditions	1	2	3	4	5
Nervous habits (nail biting, pacing, hair twirling, etc.)	1	2	3	4	5
Hair loss	1	2	3	4	5
Undiagnosable ailments	1	2	3	4	5
Other: _____	1	2	3	4	5

List all the medications you currently take and what they treat. If they're helping – great. If not, how might they be connected to your stress? Even if it seems silly or ridiculous, think out of the box.

Which symptoms on the Physical Stress Assessment did you have before 2020? Have they changed since the lockdown? If so, how?

Overall, how does your body *physically* respond to stress? There are no right or wrong answers. Just write whatever comes to mind.

More than Physical

The Physical Stress Assessment made me realize not only are my tight neck and tense shoulders barometers for my stress levels, but my teeth grinding and clenched jaw also meant something, too. I'd done both for so long that I never even saw them as problems. I still sometimes struggle with these aches and pains, but nothing like before the fire when I didn't understand my anxieties

Now, I know how to make the pain go away. Exercise is

a daily priority. Meditation is too, but I'm not as diligent about that, so my physical pain will remind me I'm not too busy to sit in silence a few minutes every day. I can tell such a difference when I take care of myself and focus on what I can control – sleep, what I eat, moving my body, having a meaningful conversation with someone every day.

We'll talk more about all this later, but the lesson here?

Small, daily choices = big changes.

What about You?

Was it surprising to see where you physically ranked high and low with your stress? Or, are you numb in certain spots, or perhaps everywhere? Begin searching for a bigger meaning with your aches and pains.

Pay attention to your body because it's a brilliant machine that functions in countless ways without a second thought on your part. You blink, you breathe, your heart beats all on its own. You don't seem to notice or appreciate the genius of your inner-workings until something goes wrong and hurts, or is not functioning properly.

Your headaches, that sore hip, your vision problems.

It all holds meaning. Your body (how you showed up to read this book today) was there when you fell off your bike in elementary school and had to get stitches, or when your first love broke your heart years ago, or endured that boss for a solid decade who did nothing but criticize you.

Your body has literally been there for each and every moment. So it makes sense that the wear and tear from a lifetime of use still shows today (not just in wrinkles and scars).

Our patterns are interconnected: physically, emotionally, behaviorally and psychologically. It's not easy to break down because they're all linked together.

Read on to learn how.

Notes

1. Levine, P. A. (1997). Waking the tiger: healing trauma. North Atlantic Books.

7. Emotions in Motion

Even before the fire, I knew my weight gain, insomnia and mood swings were problems, but I'd always been so hyper that everyone just assumed I was just 'high energy.' Including myself. My father used to tease that I had two speeds: ON and OFF.

That was just part of my Marcy-ness.

Yes, and ...

Trauma also explained why I was always hypervigilant, subconsciously looking for monsters everywhere. My dad was sweet and precious, but also erratic and angry, which always kept me on high-alert. I never realized how anxious I was until I started feeling calmer and less like a house fire.

The shift truly felt like night and day.

The change did not happen all at once and it took finding the *right* type of support. For me, it was not enough to just talk about what happened – my dad, his death, our house fire. Those stress patterns were *lodged* into my body. I needed people who could *show me* how to change, how to get unstuck and to guide me during my ups and downs as I struggled to find new thoughts and behaviors.

Jay's Story

I met Jay through an online writing community. He was a colleague and not a client. Jay was a sixty-four-year-old widower and retiree. He'd just always had jobs, but no real passion. His marriage didn't sound overly happy, and neither of his sons was speaking to him. I knew this because he complained about everything instead of writing. He showed up bitter and angry most weeks.

Jay was diagnosed with throat cancer not long after he joined our group. The doctors gave him less than three months to live and wanted to do surgery immediately to remove his vocal box. He would never hear his own voice again.

That felt like a death sentence to him, so Jay began seeking alternatives. He found a holistic nutritionist, an acupuncturist, and a trauma-informed therapist. I noticed Jay began to soften and seemed less grumpy. I actually look forward to hearing how his story of healing unfolded each week.

Everything turned around for him when he realized *nothing* he did growing up was good enough for his overly critical mom.

"It doesn't matter," he always thought. "Nothing mattered."

It was like an invisible message on how Jay saw the entire world. Subconsciously, he stopped trying in junior high, then spent the rest of his life proving his mother right.

Slowly, Jay started voicing his needs in certain areas. He apologized to his sons for his emotional unavailability as their dad and reconciled with one, while holding out hope for the other.

Time will tell the rest of Jay's journey, but he celebrated two years of being cancer-free in 2017, without surgery, chemo or anything else his original doctors wanted. Jay feels like his cancer diagnosis was a wakeup call to change. He has a girlfriend now and finally started writing his first novel.

He seemed to have found his "happily ever after."

Stress and Cancer

To me, cancer is massive stress to the body. If you or someone you care about is battling cancer or other mystery illnesses, consider reading *Radical Remission: Surviving Cancer Against All Odds* by Kelly A. Turner, PhD

While Dr. Turner was getting her doctorate at the University of California, Berkeley, she was shocked to discover that nobody had studied cases of radical (or unexpected) remission – when people recover against all odds without the help of conventional medicine, or even after traditional medicine had failed.

This sent her on a journey around the world where she interviewed over 100 radical-remission survivors, researched over 1,000 such cases; plus, spoke to holistic healers from all over the world.

In her book, Dr. Turner shares nine factors that can lead to spontaneous remission, even after conventional medicine has failed. Only two of the factors are physical, the rest are mental, emotional and spiritual.

One of the chapters explores suppressed emotions, particularly how stress and fear, are bad for your health.

She says, "Suppressed emotions are *any* emotions you are hanging on to from the past, whether positive, negative, conscious or unconscious. The most common emotions we hold on to are negative ones, such as stress, fear, trauma, regret, anger, but we may also hold on to positive emotions, such as happiness. Most assume holding on to happiness is a good thing; however, when happiness is tied to your past, it quickly turns into nostalgia, which keeps us focused on a memory of past happiness, as opposed to the possibility of actual happiness in the present."[1]

To me, *Radical Remission* should be required reading whether you have cancer or not. It's not just a story about how to heal. It explains how to avoid disease altogether.

Body Language

Stress not only affects you physically, but also emotionally. You can tell that difference because when everything is right in your world, your mood feels lighter. Freer, with a skip in your step.

On the flip side, when you're anxious or worried, you feel a dull, heavy ache inside. Maybe your stomach churns. You lumber around, if you feel anything at all. You're numb.

The entire world is experiencing this pandemic together. That is both unprecedented and incredible. Each week has brought new and scary plot twists, like a movie we're still unsure of the ending. That keeps us at the edge of our seats, but also anxious. Many of us are feeling confused, lonely, helpless, irritated, sad, frustrated, or angry these days.

The late neuropharmacologist Candace Pert said, "The body is your subconscious mind. Our physical body can be changed by the emotions we experience ... a feeling sparked in our mind-or-body will translate as a peptide being released somewhere. [Organs, tissues, skin, muscle and endocrine glands] all have peptides receptors on them and can access and store emotional information.

This means *emotional memory is stored in many places in the body, not just or even primarily in the brain.*"[2]

That is remarkable. Your emotions are stored in your brain, *and* your body.

We even use body language to describe our frustrations:

My ex makes me sick to my stomach.

My boss is such a headache.

Stop being such a pain in the neck.

She makes me want to puke.

Physical + Emotional Connection

Louise Hay was the author of the international bestseller, *Heal Your Body*. She was also the founder of Hay House Publishing, home for transformational authors like Wayne Dyer, Cheryl Richardson, and Gabrielle Bernstein.

Heal Your Body is a step-by-step guide that connects different health struggles to emotions you might be repressing, then offers tips on how to create new thought patterns.[3] This concept is revolutionary.

Illustration 2

COMMON COMPLAINTS + POSSIBLE EMOTIONS

Headaches – loss of control.
Breathing Difficulties (shallow breathing, panic attacks) – anxiety.
Voice and Throat Problems – oppression.
Neck or Shoulder Tension – burdens and responsibilities.
Heart or Chest Pains – hurts or losses (as in sadness).
Lower Back Pain – frustration or anger.
Stomach and Intestines – fear.
Insomnia – loss of self.
Fatigue – resentments.
Numbness – trauma.

Adapted from Hay, L. L. (2012). Heal your body: the mental causes for physical illness and the metaphysical way to overcome them. Hay House.

Keep Searching

Is this for real? Some swear by it, while others are doubtful. I'm not the expert, I'm just sharing alternatives with you.

However, do you have strange ailments and the doctors cannot find anything *wrong* with you?

Or, do your tests keep coming back *normal*?

If you're in pain but not finding the solutions you need, why not seek answers elsewhere?

If so, keep looking. Google *whatever is wrong with you* + alternatives.

Trust your instincts. Your health and happiness are worth the effort.

Do This!

Take the Emotion/Behaviors Stress Assessment[4] to better understand the impact of anxiety in your life.

Remember, my Book Accelerator course, *Transform Your Stress*, has all the book's exercises and assessments together in one workbook, as well as 3.5 hours worth of bonus video content:

https://marcymckay.teachable.com/p/transform-your-stress/.

EMOTIONS/BEHAVIORS STRESS ASSESSMENT

Circle each stressor that you've experienced during your lifetime.

1. Anxiety
2. Self-doubt
3. Shame
4. Guilt
5. Anger
6. Fear
7. Insomnia
8. Depression
9. Perfectionism
10. Hypervigilance
11. Procrastination
12. Work Addiction
13. Inability to Achieve Goals
14. Inability to Focus or Concentrate
15. Feeling Unworthy/Ineffective
16. Feeling Too Much/A Burden
17. Imposter's Syndrome
18. PTSD
19. Self-Harm
20. Lack of Trust in People
21. Oppositional Defiance
22. Suicidal Thoughts
23. ADD/ADHD
24. Chronic Disorganization
25. Obsessive-Compulsive Disorders
26. Bipolar Disorder
27. Alcoholism
28. Drug Addiction
29. Smoking
30. Eating Disorders
31. Promiscuity/Sex/Porn Addiction
32. Social Media/Technology Addiction
33. Shopping/Addiction to Clothes
34. Staying Busy
35. Too Much TV/Screen Addiction
36. Gambling
37. Money/Spending Addiction
38. Clinginess
39. Avoidance/Isolation
40. Chronic Illness & Pain
41. Lack of Empathy/Bullying
42. Dissociative Personality Disorders
43. Other Behavioral Disorders

Your Brain Wants to Keep You Safe

Whoa, I've easily experienced 32 out of the 43 symptoms at some point in my life. That's a lot.

What about you?

Remember me? I'm the gal who likes to play *Let's Be Honest*. We all know that life's not fair. Everyone has experienced highs and lows, but that's sometimes hard to remember while scrolling through Facebook when it seems like everyone else has found true love, is making a million bucks and their lives look so bright and shiny.

Not true.

Everyone struggles with anxiety, shame, guilt, self-doubt. These feelings are universal and part of our humanness. Since our brains are biologically hardwired to look for danger to protect us from those invisible saber-toothed tigers, we're also more prone to negativity. To spot the bad, instead of the good.

Seriously. It takes time and effort to rewire yourself for more joy, confidence and success. But it is possible. Whether you've lost your mojo like I did after our fire, or have never felt that you had value or mattered – you can change.

If. You. Do. The. Work.

Physical Pain & Emotional Pain = Same

In 2011, the National Institute of Mental Health and the National Institute on Drug Abuse funded a study where researchers discovered that physical pain and intense emotional pain affect us similarly. They focused specifically on social rejection and found the same part of the brain lights up from either kind of distress, to the point that our bodies cannot tell the difference. That means emotions can hurt us to the point we feel physical pain.[5]

It reminds me of those couples married 65 years that

when one spouse dies, the other does, too, for no apparent reason one week later. People whisper at the funeral how the latter must've died from a broken heart.

It also explains why my body hurt so much after our house fire. Why I couldn't seem to turn off the alarm in my head.

Emotions can hurt us to the point we feel physical pain.

If your aches seem worse or your unhealthy behaviors seem to be acting up more these days, it might be your suppressed emotions begging you to find a new way of responding to an unsettling situation.

Psychological Impact

Do you tend to have an *exaggerated* bias towards positivity or negativity? Think of this friend who does nothing but complain, no matter what. He's like Oscar the Grouch. Or, that other pal who seems to burst into cheers when it's clearly not the time or place. It's like she can't read the room. Set down the pom-poms.

My husband and I aren't that extreme, but we can each experience the exact same situation and I tend to see the glass as half full, while he views it as half empty. Neither of us is wrong or right, but our stress origins made us that way and I've learned to embrace our differences. He shows me the world in ways I would never see on my own. It's a blessing and not a curse.

What about you? We've talked about the past, what are your biggest struggles today?

Do This!

Take the Today's Emotions/Behaviors Stress Assessment[6] to delve more into your anxieties.

Want to enhance your learning on all this info? Check out my Book Accelerator course, *Transform Your Stress*. It has all the book's exercises and assessments together in one workbook, as well as 3.5 hours worth of bonus video content:

https://marcymckay.teachable.com/p/transform-your-stress/.

TODAY'S EMOTIONS/BEHAVIORS STRESS ASSESSMENT

Please rate each symptom on a scale of 1 - 5 as it applies to your life *currently*.

	Never	Rarely	Somewhat	Often	Always
Anxiety	1	2	3	4	5
Self-doubt	1	2	3	4	5
Shame	1	2	3	4	5
Guilt	1	2	3	4	5
Anger	1	2	3	4	5
Fear	1	2	3	4	5
Insomnia	1	2	3	4	5
Depression	1	2	3	4	5
Perfectionism	1	2	3	4	5
Hypervigilance	1	2	3	4	5
Procrastination	1	2	3	4	5
Work Addiction	1	2	3	4	5
Inability to Achieve Goals	1	2	3	4	5
Inability to Focus or Concentrate	1	2	3	4	5
Feeling Unworthy/Ineffective	1	2	3	4	5
Feeling Too Much/A Burden	1	2	3	4	5
Imposter's Syndrome	1	2	3	4	5
PTSD	1	2	3	4	5
Self-Harm	1	2	3	4	5
Lack of Trust in People	1	2	3	4	5
Oppositional Defiance	1	2	3	4	5
Suicidal Thoughts	1	2	3	4	5
ADD/ADHD	1	2	3	4	5

Chronic Disorganization	1	2	3	4	5
Obsessive-Compulsive Disorders	1	2	3	4	5
Bipolar Disorder	1	2	3	4	5
Alcoholism	1	2	3	4	5
Drug Addiction	1	2	3	4	5
Smoking	1	2	3	4	5
Eating Disorders	1	2	3	4	5
Promiscuity/Sex/Porn Addiction	1	2	3	4	5
Social Media/Technology Addiction	1	2	3	4	5
Shopping/Addiction to Clothes	1	2	3	4	5
Staying Busy	1	2	3	4	5
Too Much TV/Screen Addiction	1	2	3	4	5
Gambling	1	2	3	4	5
Money/Spending Addiction	1	2	3	4	5
Clinginess	1	2	3	4	5
Avoidance/Isolation	1	2	3	4	5
Chronic Illness & Pain	1	2	3	4	5
Lack of Empathy/Bullying	1	2	3	4	5
Dissociative Personality Disorders	1	2	3	4	5
Other Behavioral Disorder	1	2	3	4	5

If your body could talk, what would it say that these hurts mean EMOTIONALLY?

_____

_____

_____

Psychologically, are you more hardwired for positivity or negativity? If so, where do you think that bias started?

_____

_____

_____

_____

Notes

1. Turner, K. A. (2015). Radical remission: surviving cancer against all odds. HarperOne.

2. Pert, C. (2005). Your Body is Your Subconscious Mind. Louisville, Colorado; Sounds True.

3. Hay, L. L. (1984). Heal your body. Hay House.

4. Adapted from Kipp, M. (2019, February 20). 26 symptoms of hidden emotional trauma? Do you have any? Mastin Kipp. https://mastinkipp.com/26-symptoms-of-hidden-emotional-trauma-do-you-have-any/.

5. Ethan Kross, Marc G. Berman, Walter Mischel, Edward E. Smith, Tor D. Wager. "Social Rejection Shares Somatosensory Representations with Physical Pain." Proceedings of the National Academy of Sciences, online, April 12, 2011. https://www.pnas.org/content/108/15/6270

6. Adapted from Kipp, M. (2019, February 20). 26 symptoms of hidden emotional trauma? Do you have any? Mastin Kipp. https://mastinkipp.com/26-symptoms-of-hidden-emotional-trauma-do-you-have-any/.

8. Stress Busters

My dad sold Caterpillar tractors and traveled a lot during the workweek. It the early 1980s, he was in Houston on routine business. It was broad daylight as he lugged a briefcase full of wrenches and other tools back to his car in a parking garage. He'd just set the satchel in his open trunk when he felt a sharp poke in his back.

It was a gun. A deep voice demanded money.

The robber had been on a recent crime spree, targeting overweight people.

He picked the wrong guy because Roy Mason considered himself to be Bad, Bad Leroy Brown, the baddest man in the whole damn town.

My father raised both his arms in surrender. "My wallet is in my briefcase. Let me get it."

Dad slowly grabbed the handle of his briefcase with both hands, swung and backhanded his attacker so hard that it knocked the man off his feet. The pistol flew one way, while the guy went the other.

Terrified, my father dove onto him, banging his head against the concrete. A woman stumbled upon the scene, screaming at my dad to stop. He shouted that he was the victim and to go call the cops. I'm not sure she believed him, but she disappeared. The police arrived soon after, hailing my dad a hero.

I love this story because I picture my dad thinking he was all *Miami Vice*, but it also illustrates life isn't always what it seems. That woman was certain my father was attacking some poor fellow.

Yes, and ...

The same is true for our feelings.

Let's Press Pause

When I finally saw my full patterns and behaviors, I felt like such a train wreck. *OMG! I've ruined my kids! Why didn't my husband leave me years ago? I'm so #$%@!*

If you feel that way or something similar, let me remind you what a rock star you are.

You may not feel that strength right now, but whatever has happened to you – you're still standing. No matter how unfair, wrong, unhealthy, abusive, horrific, or unimaginable it was – you survived.

That makes you resilient.

Dictionary.com defines resilient as, "Able to withstand or recover quickly from difficult situations."

Please take a deep breath and give yourself a well-deserved break if you need one. Some people panic at this point and may want to quit reading.

Don't stop!

Stick with me, even if your discomfort is rising, or you've gone numb altogether. Recognize this may be one of your stress patterns keeping you stuck, frustrated, and unable to move forward. It may be still replaying an old story from long ago.

I understand that inner tug-of-war.

Simply put, your stress won't go away until you deal with your past. You may think you've compartmentalized your pain and tucked it away forever, but it's oozing out or erupting in other ways.

You can either deal with the messiness of your stress directly, or deal with the messiness of it indirectly through unresolved physical-and-emotional pain. The second is even harder and messier to clean up the collateral damage for you and those around you.

Your choice.

Stress Busters Toolbox

Oddly enough, your current anxieties are actually good news. They're messengers that have been trying to tell you something was "off" in your life, but nobody ever taught you how to speak the language.

Until now.

What's something you can do to lift your spirits today? An activity that's fun or nurturing, free or inexpensive to bust through your stress, such as:

1. *Watch a funny sitcom, or a fun romantic comedy.*
2. *Make a cup of hot tea and read a great book, or magazine.*
3. *Call or text a friend.*
4. *Connect with nature.*
5. *Listen to an inspiring podcast.*
6. *Move your body – crank up the music and dance, go for a walk, exercise.*

7. *Yoga class (online or social-distancing in-person).*
8. *Take a hot bath or shower.*
9. *Play with a pet.*
10. *Create – paint, draw, write.*

Think of this as a self-care toolbox because moving out of stress is a combination of two important aspects of healing. First, solo-activities you do by yourself are called **self-regulation**. You're with yourself all the time, so you might need to learn how to manage your emotional states better. To work your way out of those deep purple funks we all fall into sometimes.

Secondly, activities you *enjoy* with others (whether it's a person, a pet, or a group), is called **co-regulation**. We're also hardwired for connection and community. We long to be back with our tribe, to return to some semblance of normal. There are times when you feel down or struggling, but talking to a buddy can help you feel less blue.

Now that our two kids are back at college, we call, text or FaceTime them often. We also hold family Zoom calls every few weeks where we play a ridiculously fun card game called Exploding Kittens on our phones together (currently, the app costs $1.99 per phone, but the joy it brings is priceless). I'm sure we look silly with all four heads buried into our phones during game time, but the trash-talking, teasing and laughter are worth it.

Plus, I'm able to sneak in one serious, "Are you okay?" each time. Seeing my babies warms my mama heart.

Everyone has their go-to strategies to feel better. Some are healthy, such as walking around the park, while others are not, like too many glasses of vino, or buying stuff online that you don't need or with money you don't have to waste.

Me playing cards with my family is healthy, while me slathering butter onto a tortilla, then shoving it into my mouth is not.

If you tend to be a loner, then you're used to flying solo. Your challenge is to emotionally stretch yourself by creating more safe connections with others. Not just any people – the right people. Those who bring out the best in you.

On the other hand, if you seem to always need to be with others to feel better, then you need to work on enjoying more time alone. Find activities that encourage you to keep going.

Both self-regulation and co-regulation are crucial life skills.

I warned you this work was hard at times, but you can do this. You're stronger than you think. Just take it one imperfect step at a time.

Rachel's Transformation

Remember Rachel? She grew up with a narcissistic mom. Even though Rachel was such a hard worker and pretty much all smiles, internally, her mother's abuse and abandonment left deeps wounds. Rachel still felt like the lonely girl who didn't fit into her own family.

Even before the pandemic, her husband was content to just sit home and watch TV, but Rachel wanted more. To go out and do fun activities. Plus, mentally he was slipping farther away. She couldn't stop his health crisis, so she focused more on taking care of herself. In 2019, she started to enjoy hot baths more, spent time with her dog, rode her motorcycle, got pedicures, made lunch dates with friends.

Any sort of self-care felt new and uncomfortable for Rachel, but she still tried to do life differently. Solo endeavors felt safer because she'd been so hurt by her mom and ex-husband, but she took baby steps to do more with others and watched her self-worth grow as well.

You can do the same.

Become Brain Savvy

I began using the Brain Savvy app (free!) in March 2020. It's fast, simple and easy to understand. I quickly became a fan, which says a lot since I try to steer clear of too much technology (I have a wee bit of an addictive personality).

Now, I check-in to Brain Savvy multiple times a day. In under 60 seconds, it tells me if I'm focused, distracted or checked out, then guides me on what I need to do to reach a higher mindset.

The app also shows me how to master six core health habits for optimal physical energy: sleep, sunshine, eating, drinking, exercise and connection (we'll discuss these in greater detail later). Plus, Brain Savvy lets me easily monitor my progress, giving me more self-awareness on where I need to improve.

I was so impressed with the app that I wanted to meet the brains behind Brain Savvy.

Melissa Hallmark Kerr, PhD, is the co-creator of the app, with over 25 years of experience of health and human performance. Her clients include NASA, Purina, and the Naval Academy.

We had a great conversation, but here's what impacted

me most. When I asked Dr. Kerr about her app's success, she said, "Life is about relationships. Brain Savvy teaches people how to connect more and collide less."[1]

Those are skills we need more to not just survive a global pandemic, but to thrive long after.

Do This!

Make a list of free or inexpensive activities that lift your spirits for your Stress Busters Toolbox. You're welcome to use any that I mentioned to get started. Try to include both solo and group activities for self-regulation and co-regulation. Also to include new things you'd like to try.

_____

_____

_____

_____

_____

_____

_____

Keep adding to your toolbox and refer back to it often because self-care should be a priority in overcoming your stress.

Pick one activity and do it today.

Notes

1. Kerr, M. H., (2020, September 21). personal communication.

PART III

THE SCIENCE BEHIND YOUR STRESS

9. Because ... Science

I was a solid A-B student growing up, but I was still smart enough in high school to walk across the physics classroom and ask one of the A+ kids to be my lab partner (thank you, Brainiac Michael). Patient, funny and kind, he always explained things in a way that this right-brained gal could understand.

We're now going to talk about the science behind your stress. It's been the main missing link for you.

DO. NOT. SKIP. THIS. CHAPTER.

Please don't think – *science, snooze! Just give me steps 1-2-3 on how to feel better.*

Or, if you jumped ahead to this chapter before completing any of the Do This! assignments, go back and complete them now. The information here won't make as much sense without pinpointing exactly how your anxiety is impacting you.

Even though I first learned about neuroscience from Dr. Mellin in 2011, the biology of the brain didn't come alive for me until months after our house fire when I discovered Mastin Kipp's work in 2019, author of *Claim Your Power*. He's one of Oprah's top thought leaders. I guess I was finally in enough pain to get the message.

It's all about polyvagal theory. "Poly" means "many" and "vagal" means "wandering." Your vagus nerve starts at the back of your brain and runs down your entire spine. It plays a central role in your emotional regulation, social connection and fear responses. You know...the key ingredients to success.

Dr. Stephen Porges is a "Distinguished University Scientist" at the Kinsey Institute, who wrote the bestselling book, *The Polyvagal Theory: Neurophysiological Foundations of Emotions, Attachment, Communication, and Self-regulation.*

This world-renowned research has this to say, "If you want to improve the world, start by making people feel safer."[1]

Think of neuroscience as the science of safety.

Deb Dana, LCSW, is a therapist who showed the mental-health community how to apply Dr. Porges' work into their practices, and better serve their clients. Her book, *The Polyvagal Theory in Therapy: Engaging the Rhythm of Regulation*, is considered groundbreaking.

That's just it. These advances in neuroscience are cutting edge and still making their way into the mainstream conversation, but you're one of the cool kids who knows about this information now.

Millions of folks have felt like a mess since 2020. There's nothing wrong with YOU – it's your autonomic nervous system.

Auto-what?!

Illustration 3

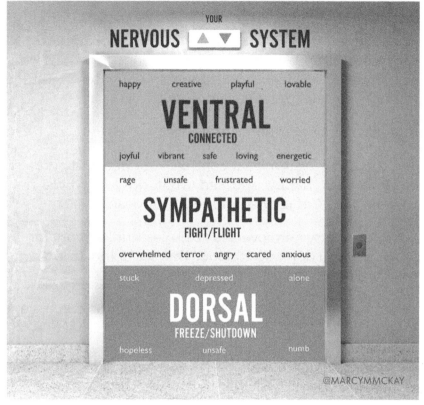

© 2020 Marcy McKay. Graphics – McCollum, R. Adapted from Porges, S.W., Dana, D. & Kipp, M.

Your Elevator is Stuck

The vagus nerve is a primary component of your autonomic nervous system. Autonomic means involuntary or unconscious. Your autonomic nervous system is made up of billions of nerve fibers that silently move up and down inside you like an elevator, day and night.

Billions.

It does this automatically. Your nervous system controls bodily functions like your breathing, heartbeat, digestive processes, all your 'going to the bathroom' functions, your sex organs and sexual responses, body temperature, metabolism, electrolyte balance, sweat and saliva.

Plus, all of your emotional responses.

Yes, the same system that controls your pee and poo, also controls your happy and sad. That gives a whole new meaning to, *"Get your sh*t together,"* doesn't it?

Your nervous system oversees a huge chunk of your inner-workings. You don't even notice that it's doing its job, *until* there's a problem:

When you hear shocking news and cannot catch your breath.

When your allergies bother you and your eyes won't stop watering.

When your heart feels out of rhythm for so long – you notice it and hopefully, go to the doctor.

Cutting-edge research now shows that your nervous system not only handles all those bodily functions, but it also houses your beliefs, thoughts, emotions and behaviors. This happens by moving in sequence between three emotional states: **ventral, sympathetic,** and **dorsal**.

Picture the colors of a light – green, yellow and red.

GREEN means GO.

YELLOW means both PAUSE and SPEED UP (because you

know you've sped through at least one intersection when the traffic light was yellow).

RED means STOP.

The Purpose of Your Autonomic Nervous System

Your autonomic nervous system has just one job, to keep you safe. Remember, our brains and bodies still think we're cavemen, battling those saber-toothed tigers. Your nervous system silently scans the world around you for danger (real or perceived). You don't even think about this. Your nervous system works on autopilot to size up everything: SAFE. UNSAFE. SAFE. UNSAFE.

It's why you panic when you receive that unexpected, expensive bill – UNSAFE.

It's why you smile back at the stranger who grins and opens the door for you – SAFE.

It's why you see that look from a loved one, you ask, "What's wrong?" – UNSAFE.

This also explains your heightened stress during the Coronavirus – UNSAFE.

Every government of every country determined COVID-19 was a threat – UNSAFE.

Invisible threat – UNSAFE.

More and more people testing positive – UNSAFE.

More and more people dying from the disease – UNSAFE.

World shutting down – UNSAFE.

Worrying about you, your family, your finances – UNSAFE.

Isolated from each other – UNSAFE.

Disruption of your regular routines – UNSAFE.

The rules are constantly changing these days – UNSAFE.

Debate over masks – UNSAFE.

Combine that with all the other disruptions in the U.S. (a nasty presidential election, all the civil unrest, bickering among family, friends and strangers) – SUPER UNSAFE!

Are you understanding why you might feel so much more stressed these days?

Plus, anxiety is highly contagious. You might be okay, but then you talk or see others who are panicked, then WHAMMO! Now, you're freaked out, too.

Danger, Will Robinson! Danger!

You get rattled, then it spreads to others – well, like a virus.

Here are your nervous system's three states:

Ventral, also called Parasympathetic (Green – Connection)

Happy. Active. Doing work you enjoy (professionally, hobbies, volunteering). Spending time with people you like or love. Going with the flow. Connection with others. Play, or relaxation. Happiness. Ventral is not some magical La La Land where problems do not exist, however, you feel more secure and can think through the issues clear enough to explore your options.

If you've had ventral moments since 2020, you definitely felt concerned, but you were also able to experience some of the unexpected blessings. Focusing more on yourself and loved ones without so many distractions. This gave you clarity on what you value most, so you began working to make your life more balanced.

People are struggling to stay in ventral these days.

Of course, we are. Our nervous systems are busy battling lions and tigers and bears.

Oh my!

Sympathetic (Yellow – Fight/Flight)

Sympathetic has a wide range from the flight responses: stressed, anxious, overwhelmed with a job you love and are quite successful at ... all the way to the fight responses: irritation, anger, rage. Too much energy. You've got to move.

Americans *worship* sympathetic. You worked 70 hours this week?

Big deal, I worked over 80 hours.

Remember, it's not all bad stress. Good stress includes traveling, weddings, the butterflies you feel when you speak before a group. Good stress serves as motivation, drive and inspiration.

Stressful stress: you worry about paying the bills, your

strained marriage, all your unfinished work, guilt about letting the kids have so much screen time, guilt that you're even complaining since so many people have it so much worse.

Again, sympathetic can be all over the emotional map.

Abuse is No Excuse

You do not get a hall pass for inflicting abuse on yourself or others. Although trauma explains so many inappropriate behaviors, it is *never* an excuse for illegal, immoral or unethical behavior.

Ever.

Dorsal (Red – Freeze or Shutdown)

Dorsal can be anything from sitting on the couch and binge-watching 16 hours of Netflix, to just low energy or apathy, to overdrinking every day or just on weekends, to isolating from family and friends. You may go to a job every week, walk and talk and exist in this world, yet inside you feel completely numb, checked-out, disconnected, shutdown, hopeless or alone.

That's dorsal.

Maybe you don't want to get out of bed. Dark thoughts consume your brain. Depressed. You can feel any of these emotions for a few moments, to weeks, months, or years. You can be fully awake, but also like the walking dead inside. That's dorsal, too.

All of the above has applied to us at some point, and then some.

No shame. This has been scary for sure.

Most of the world is bouncing between sympathetic and dorsal these days, but more ventral moments are absolutely possible. Sympathetic and dorsal are where "hurts stacked on top of hurts" really come into play.

That is why it's so important to understand your own stress patterns, so you learn how to get back to ventral faster, or at least up a little higher on the elevator of your nervous system.

The House at Pooh Corner

To better illustrate your nervous system, let's use A.A Milne's childhood classic, *Winnie the Pooh*. Each character personifies a different emotional state.

Ventral (connected) – Winnie the Pooh. That silly ol' bear is loving and connected. Sure, he fumbles and bumbles around, but he can find the bright side to most anything.

Sympathetic (fight or flight) – Tigger and Piglet – are opposite ends of sympathetic. Piglet is all anxious and fearful, *ohhhh, da-dear!* While Tigger bounces off the walls nonstop, with happy but nervous energy. *Boing, boing, boing!* Tigger is not really a fighter, but he's more apt to argue than Piglet, who is pure flight.

Dorsal (freeze or shutdown) – Eeyore. That pin-the-tail on the donkey is depression on four legs. *Oh bother, why even try?* I've always appreciated how Pooh and the others love and accept Eeyore just for who he is.

Pooh = ventral.

Piglet = sympathetic (flight).

Tigger = sympathetic (fight).

Eeyore = dorsal.

If you have questions, like how to change your stress patterns and more, keep reading because *this* is the answer you've been searching for – your nervous system.

Do This!

Look at Your Nervous System Elevator (Illustration 3) for the emotions you feel in your three emotional states, and add other feelings that describe you.

Ventral – Connected:

_____

_____

Sympathetic – Fight/Flight:

_____

_____

Dorsal – Freeze/Shutdown:

_____

_____

What did you learn about your nervous system that you didn't know before?

_____

_____

Notes

1. Porges, S. W. (2011). The polyvagal theory: neurophysiological foundations of emotions, attachment, communication, and self-regulation. Norton.

10. Nervous System 101

I grew up watching *Schoolhouse Rock!* Animated educational videos that taught us grammar, math and civics during commercial breaks of our Saturday morning cartoons. The Powers That Be were clever enough to sneak in learning between episodes of *Scooby Do* and *The Great Grape Ape*.

This song should be sung to the tune of "I'm Just a Bill."

Ventral means GO!

Sympathetic means WHOAH!

And, dorsal means oh baby, NO, NO, NOOO!

If you've got the cash to turn "Go-Whoah-No!" into a music video, then call me. I'm sure we'll be rich.

I've always joked that I married my father and my husband married his mother, so when we got together – it was Family Feud. We've had pretty much the same arguments since day one, but the trauma from our house fire brought a new level of pain I'd never experienced before.

I unraveled in unexpected ways. I had to show both my brain *and* my body countless times, in countless ways, to move beyond my perfectionism and over care-taking. That I didn't have to spend hours writing and rewriting the same email. It was okay if there were typos. That I did not have to be the "fixer" of everyone's problems, that it was okay to wake up feeling calmer.

These were monumental shifts for me, but none more so than in my marriage where I learned to stop emotionally holding my husband at arm's length since that's how I managed my dad's intensity as a child.

The list goes on and on how my life has improved, but *let's be honest* – surviving grammatical errors was much easier than working on emotional intimacy.

Your Nervous System Can't Skip Ahead

Just as an elevator cannot jump ahead from the basement up to the thirty-ninth floor, your emotional regulation must move through the other required states first. The pattern is predictable. That means you cannot bypass dorsal (freeze/shutdown) to get straight to ventral (connection).

You must first move through sympathetic (yellow- fight/ flight) to get that higher state. You also **cannot** avoid being triggered. This will bother my perfectionists, but it's true. You'll always be triggered multiple times every day, but now you're learning there's nothing wrong with you.

You just need to get back on track.

This is GREAT NEWS! It explains WHY you've been unable to change in the past, like there was an invisible wall inside stopping you. Your nervous system deemed those thoughts and behaviors as UNSAFE, even if they seem silly or irrational to you.

Just tell her no.

Just put up your new website.

Just go exercise more.

Just believe you deserve more.

Just stop eating carbs.

Just get a better attitude.

Just start saving more money.

Just stop dating losers.

Just do it.

That doesn't work. You cannot simply talk yourself into change. It has to come from the inside out – your body, not just your brain, must feel safe enough to make those changes, no matter how big or small they seem.

This is why you need support – friends cheering you along the way, in addition to a knowledgeable guide to show you how it's done. To help you begin again when you have setbacks, U-turns, get off track or fall back to your old ways. Mistakes are absolutely part of the process and always will be.

Here's another truth bomb. We now understand that emotions are stored in our body in addition to our brains, and the nerve fibers along our spine serve as the communicators between the two.

Think about how much bigger your body is than your brain? That means 80% of your internal messaging comes from your body to your brain, while only 20% come from your brain to your body.

The stuckness you feel, that invisible wall of fear that won't let you gain any momentum or change at all?

That is stress still stuck in your body from long ago.

Intentions Are Not Enough

It does not *matter* how much therapy you've had, how often you listen to uplifting podcasts or TED Talks, or how many positive affirmations you repeat daily, etc.

DOES. NOT. MATTER.

Those activities are great and you should keep them up if they help you stay motivated, but now you're learning there's more to the story since most self-help modalities are mainly connected to your brain. Your body, which is your subconscious mind, is still holding onto to those stress origins and didn't know how to change in the past. You've repeated those same patterns in different ways over the years.

We're Not Talking Rational

If your fear feels completely irrational, like you want to throw up, have a heart attack, drop dead, go completely numb or experience some other feeling that seems silly, trivial, ridiculous or even extreme, then BINGO!

Congratulations. You've discovered one of your unhealthy patterns. Your job is to now show your nervous system that it's okay to change.

That it's safe to ...

Feel worthy.

Lose that extra 50 pounds for good.

Start your dream biz.

Stop putting everyone else ahead of you.

Be closer to your wife of 20 years.

Trust your intuition.

You do not have to binge, or purge.

You don't have to cut (self-harm).

Quit abusing alcohol once and for all.

Get out of a toxic relationship.

Yes, you can JUST DO IT, but only after you understand where your stress patterns have left you stuck, so you can retrain brain and body.

That is where and how you change for good.

Stop Resisting Your Emotions

This concept is so freeing. Stop fearing, resisting, resenting, or hating what you consider to be *negative* or *bad* emotions. That took me a while to appreciate since I was Susie Sunshine and felt like I was doing something *wrong* or *bad* when I felt afraid, sad or had hurt feelings. Emotions that my father considered weak.

On the flip side, many people struggle to let in positive feelings. That makes perfect sense if you've felt unworthy, unimportant, or that you somehow didn't matter or weren't good enough in the past.

Once again, this process is not one size fits all. Listen to what speaks true to you. If you're all about your vision board or setting intentions, but still are not manifesting your desires ... this could be why. Your nervous system doesn't feel SAFE to make those changes.

This is also the best news.

Why?

Because it also takes the shame out of the equation.

You're not lame.

You're not a loser.

You're not lazy.

There is nothing wrong with you. Something in your subconscious, the thoughts beneath your thoughts, still feels UNSAFE about the very changes you want to make.

Science says so.

Learn to welcome, respect, appreciate, love, and value all your emotions equally because they're just doing their job. Keeping you SAFE. Plus, now you're learning you have the power to change. To be less stressed and to start making your dreams come true.

Repeat the new pattern, the new way of thinking, doing and being, until it no longer scares the bageezus out of you.

This is a simple, but not easy process.

Do This!

With what you've learned about your nervous system, *which* patterns have you been unable to change?

_____

_____

Here are other questions to consider:

In what areas, do you think you've subconsciously marked as UNSAFE?

_____

_____

What emotions do you consider UNSAFE?

_____

_____

What emotions in your job have you labeled UNSAFE?

_____

_____

What emotions in your romantic relationship(s), past or present, have you labeled UNSAFE?

_____

_____

What other areas of life do you struggle to feel SAFE to have a variety of emotions?

_____

Which people in your life feel SAFE/UNSAFE?

_____

_____

What activities help you feel SAFE/UNSAFE?

_____

_____

11. Your Home Away from Home

Back when the world still passed for n-o-r-m-a-l in January 2020, I started using Zoom for online meetings for my group coaching. At first, recording the live sessions stressed me out to point that I wanted to throw up (a sympathetic response – fight or flight), all day leading up to the video call. I hated looking foolish in front of my clients as they watched me fumble around with the buttons.

It upset me, but just telling myself, *it's okay, it's not that big a deal, or you can do this* was not enough to calm my nerves. Not even close.

I had to actually do it. More than once. I improved a bit each time and gained more confidence weekly. During quarantining, all my client appointments moved online, so I became a Zoom pro. Now, the thought of recording on Zoom no longer makes me want to upchuck.

This is where *support* is vital. In looking back I was able to get over my fear of using Zoom pretty easy. I watched videos and talked to my techy friends for advice, but changing the unhealthy patterns in my marriage required a much higher level of support.

I've worked closely with my life coach to pinpoint precise behaviors, thought patterns and the different sensations in my body when I feel triggered and am in fight/flight/ flee mode. My husband was paying the price for me still subconsciously rebelling against my father.

Changing myself has made me a happier woman, wife, mom, sister, daughter, friend and colleague. Mark and I still trigger each other, then we realize our nervous systems are playing Family Feud again. We're just repeating old habits.

We say *I'm sorry* much faster now, so we can get back to *I love you.*

Awkward and Weird

We all hate looking inexperienced or foolish, but that's standard when learning anything new, or growing in different ways.

Every. Time. Whatever unhealthy thoughts and behaviors that make up your stress patterns, you must do it in small, ugly baby steps to feel less vulnerable. Repeat the process until the fear or resistance no longer has power over you.

Here are a few other examples:

Despite the knots in your stomach when you think about billing your clients, you send their invoices immediately after completing a job. You stop procrastinating. They pay and start feeling your value.

Even though you feel shaky and nauseous, you call your 40-year-old son to say you will no longer pay his bills. He needs to get a job. You set a boundary and survive his anger. It's easier sometimes than others, yet you keep at it and don't back down.

You sense that your monthly migraines mean something more than just being bed-ridden for days. You find a trauma-informed practitioner who understands how the nervous system works to help you feel more regulated, more often.

You sit down and start writing that novel you've always wanted to create, even though self-doubt trails you the whole way. You just do it.

You realize overeating and drinking too much subconsciously kept you attached to your mom, whom you adored because she was the life of the party. You understand why you always sabotaged yourself. You didn't want to go against your family.

My client Nicole thought she'd have a heart attack when she first began standing up to her coworker at the office. For Rachel, numb was so much a part of her life that it took time for her to feel anything other than pure loneliness. Happiness and self-worth seemed foreign to her.

They both changed, and you can, too.

Home Away from Home

I love this term by Deb Dana – *home away from home.* I participated in a live Q&A with her while attending a coaching conference in Scottsdale, Arizona in 2019.

Deb is soft-spoken, funny and wise (yes, I refer to her by her first name like we do virtual coffee). She talked to us from what I assume is her home office with a framed photograph of the brain hanging over her left and a large glass jar full of dark rocks sitting on a shelf to the right. That sums up Deb Dana beautifully – she's the perfect balance between science and woo-woo.

In talking about our nervous systems, she says, "Each autonomic state brings up a characteristic range of responses through its own pattern of **protection** or **connection**."[1]

Everything we think, say, or do is about protection or connection.

In an interview with fellow therapist Jason Sunseri, Deb talks about how even though your nervous system has three emotional states, you tend to run back to a particular "home away from home" when stressed, anxious, fearful, angry or dysregulated in any way.[2]

Subconsciously, your brain and body are screaming – UNSAFE. That dysregulation stems from your stress origins (Chapter 4).

Me? I've pretty much spent my life in sympathetic (fight or flight). Sure, it seemed great because I could get sh*t done all day, but I tortured myself and everyone around me with my perfectionism, overthinking and worrying. Those same coping strategies were also wrecking my health. When I'm really ramped up, I call that my "screaming sympathetic."

My husband encouraged me to stop my out-of-control ways with helpful comments like, *just don't worry about it – who cares what she thinks? Blow it off.*

Neither of us understood those behaviors had been *hardwired* into my body since childhood. I wanted to stop, but I could not.

Until I learned how.

With the right support, I learned new ways to respond and change my unhealthy patterns. It was the magical formula I'd always wanted.

That's why I'm sharing this now because everything we think, say or do is about protection or connection.

Your Insides Don't Always Match Your Outsides

As Susie Sunshine, I looked like I stayed in ventral (connected), with a smile on my face, happy and encouraging. Sometimes, that was true, but other times, it was a mask. Now, does that mean every funny story I ever told or sincere gesture of mine was fake or a lie?

Of course not, but I also never realized how much anxiety controlled me. When something went wrong with someone else (their relationship fell apart, a death in their family, a problem at work, or they faced some sort of crisis or struggle), my nervous system felt triggered. It's like electricity shot through my entire body and my brain screamed, *Gotta fix it now! It's MY JOB to fix this! I CANNOT be okay, until you are okay!*

The pattern started with my dad, but continued throughout my life. The more I cared about the person, the more triggered I felt by their stress. I used to do that a lot, even when the situation was clearly not my problem, or I should mind my own business.

Sympathetic is still my home away from home, but nothing like before since now I understand what's happening and can get myself back to ventral (connected). I'm actually in a much healthier place to help others now, because I don't feel responsible to solve the entire planet's problems.

This also explains why so many of you feel triggered these

days, your nervous system is shouting, *Gotta fix it now!* Subconsciously, you're still carrying the weight of the world on your shoulders and feel responsible for everyone else's pain.

Here's another example. Famed comedian Robin Williams was an Academy-Award winning actor. He was so talented, funny and kind; the man was truly beloved by all.

On the outside, he was the life of the party and seemed pure ventral, but so much of his frantic energy was sympathetic. Humor was his mask. He mentioned during interviews on occasion that he struggled with depression and addiction, which are both very dorsal activities, but then Williams would joke about it and the conversation would move on elsewhere. His suicide indicates that dorsal was his home away from home.

Smiling depression is real.

Uh, I Needed to Change by Yesterday

How long does it take to change emotional states?

That depends on the situation, how long it has been a go-to coping strategy, and how deeply it's wired into your brain and body. Plus, your support system. It just depends.

Remember, the key to change is time, patience and practice. This means you must do the very thing that scares you, maybe even terrifies you, until you've exhausted the pattern. The bigger the pattern, the more support you need.

Just doing it differently, over and over, helps your nervous system subconsciously move that thought or behavior from UNSAFE to SAFE inside you.

The Email from Hell

Here's a small example of how quickly your nervous system moves between emotional states. It's a regular day, or what passes for normal during a global pandemic, so you already wake up feeling more anxious than usual. You didn't sleep well, so you're already out of sorts. What bad news will you see online today?

Still, you're having a decent day (ventral – connected), when you fire up your laptop in your makeshift office in your guest room and check your email. WHAMMO! The first message you read is from that jack-wagon of a person from work who is always causing problems. You groan the second you see his or her name, your blood pressure rises and your heart beats faster.

Now, you're in sympathetic (fight or flight), imagining all the horrible ways this scenario will end. Fuming over the trouble with this person. Ten minutes later, a friend happens to call. You two laugh and visit for ten minutes, so when you hang up, you're back in ventral.

This time, you reread the email and can still see that person is a jack-wagon, but now you just deal with it and move on. You don't let it ruin your day.

If the email upset you so much that you went into dorsal (freeze or shutdown) – maybe you take days to respond to the email. Maybe you don't respond at all, even though it was important and you should have taken care of it.

You. Just. Couldn't.

I know that sounds irrational, but we all have examples of things we do that make no sense. Except *now* you understand why you didn't change before, and how you can now. It's truly transformative.

Safety is the Key

Uhhhh, what?! That confused me the first time I read about "safety" in healing emotional wounds. I thought, *of course, I felt safe growing up. My parents loved me. Nobody locked me in the basement.*

Please note, there was no basement in my house growing up, but that's another story. I've since learned that subconsciously, we view the world today depending on how safe and connected we felt as children with our caregivers on a consistent basis.

When it comes to trauma, I had to acknowledge since I never knew which dad I would encounter – *fun, moody, sulky, irritated or raging* – my father was both SAFE and UNSAFE to my family. I did not have the language for it as a child, but his dysregulated nervous system always left me dysregulated. Whether or not he was okay dictated the same for me, which kept me in constant inner turmoil (sympathetic – fight or flight). You can hurt or heal someone a thousand different ways without ever raising a finger.

Safety is everything.

When I say "safe", I realize most people aren't putting a gun to your head, but what's your internal energy when you're around them?

Depending on what the situation calls for, do you feel calmer, happier, more energized, more connected?

Is it okay to be the *real* you around them, and not someone else you pretend to be?

Not performing or playing a part, but just be you – warts and all?

Do they have your best interest at heart?

Or, are they genuinely "safe," but your insides are still stuck in perceived danger from the past?

Only you can answer this.

Setbacks are Part of the Process

Your nervous system will always resist change, even positive ones, because that's how it works. Until you prove to both your body and your brain these new ways of doing, being and thinking are SAFE it will resist the very changes you're trying to make.

Expect resistance, mistakes and setbacks.

Three steps forward and two steps back.

When, not *if*, this happens understand that you are *not* failing, you're right on track. It's all part of the process.

#$%@!

It's okay if your brain feels scrambled at this point. That

confusion may be one of your old coping strategies as your nervous system processes this new information. It senses that you want to change, so it's trying to shut that down and keep you stuck. It wants to keep you SAFE.

Be patient. Your home away from home will always be part of you, but you can still grow and expand in ways you never dreamed possible.

Do This!

Which emotional state is your emotional home away from home?

Ventral (connection)

Sympathetic (fight or flight).

Dorsal (freeze or shutdown).

Why do you think that is?

_____

_____

_____

Have you started making some changes and what happened?

_____

_____

What situations tend to send you to your home away from home?

_____

_____

_____

What's your biggest takeaway so far about how your nervous system operates?

_____

_____

_____

_____

Notes

1. Dana, D. (2018). The polyvagal theory in therapy: engaging the rhythm of regulation. W.W. Norton & Company.
2. Sunseri, J. (2019, August 27). Deb Dana Interview: Story Follows State, Climbing the Ladder & Diagnosis. JustinLMFT. other, Polyvagal Podcast. https://www.justinlmft.com/post/debdanainterview.

12. Attachment is Everything

Understanding how my nervous system was connected to all my post-fire struggles, attachment styles explained the rest of my internal puzzle. The quirks of my marriage, my husband's family and mine. Plus, all the generations before us. Why this relative was emotionally distant, why that one could never say no to another's drinking, or why somebody's inability to be alone meant she needed constant companionship like a human security blanket.

Suddenly, everyone's weirdness made sense.

I don't mean that disrespectfully – your family is weird, too. I firmly believe we're all a bit kooky, but whatever weird you grew up with feels *normal*. Your weird doesn't look like mine.

Attachment Styles

The psychological theory of attachment was created by Dr. John Bowlby, a British psychoanalyst who researched the effects of separation between infants and their parents in the 1950s. Attachment explains our relationships to people, places and things (money, work, social media, everything). Up to 90% of our attachment history stems from – you guessed it, childhood.[1]

That means the patterns we created as kids follow us into

adulthood, where those coping strategies repeat in a variety of ways until we create healthier ones.

Think back to the elevator illustration of your nervous system (Chapter 9). There are the three, predictable stages where our emotions happen in order: ventral (connected), sympathetic (fight or flight), or dorsal (freeze or shutdown).

Everyone has different coping strategies, and there are areas where our elevator is stuck in fight-flight-freeze, or we're like that scratched record playing the same part of the song over and over.

Your *attachment* history informs:

1. How worthy you feel.
2. How much you trust others.
3. How well you connect with others (i.e. communication, conflict, socializing).

Diane Poole Heller, PhD and her mentor, Dr. Levine, are both considered to be pioneers in attachment theory. Her book, *The Power of Attachment – How to Create Deep and Lasting Intimate Relationships*, does a terrific job of explaining how to restore those broken connections caused from the past in easy-to-follow language. I highly recommend it.

Dr. Heller says we are fundamentally designed to heal. "Even if our childhood is less than ideal, our secure system is biologically programmed in us, and our job is to simply find out what's interfering with it – and learn what we can do to make those secure tendencies more dominant."[2]

The 4 Attachment Styles:

Secure.

Anxious.

Avoidant.

Disorganized.

Dr. Heller uses the term "ambivalent" instead of 'anxious', but several experts prefer "anxious" because it's easier to understand. Really, I don't care for the last three names because they all sound shaming, but again, nobody asked my opinion.

The Power of Attachment also explains that in the wake of a traumatic event such as a car accident, severe illness, loss of a loved one, or experience of abuse – your attachment style deeply influences what happens next for you.

Like a house fire or whatever crisis you're facing. Big or small.

Illustration 4

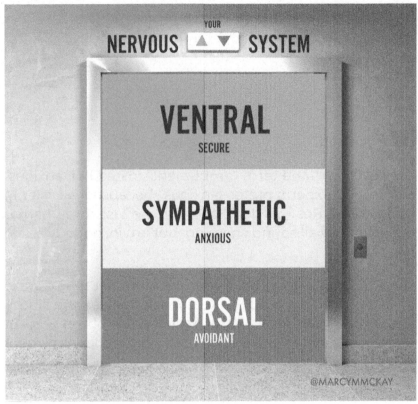

© 2020 Marcy McKay. Graphics – McCollum, R. Adapted from Porges, S.W., Dana, D., Poole Heller, D. & Kipp, M.

Returning to the House at Pooh Corner's

Learning about attachment styles can feel like learning a new language. Think back to the characters from *Winnie the Pooh* to better understand these concepts:

- Secure – Winnie the Pooh.
- Anxious – Piglet.
- Avoidant – Eeyore.
- Disorganized – Tigger.

As I explain each attachment style, I'm also going to say "parents" for simplicity's sake, though this applies to whatever adults were dominant in your upbringing.

We're all multi-faceted, so look for parts of your personality in each attachment style. These are not *personality styles*, but how you *attach* to other people, places and things.

It's all about relationships and connection.

Secure

Think Winnie the Pooh.

On the elevator of your nervous system, it's ventral (connected).

Secure is the ideal attachment style because as children, they had a consistent, loving environment. Not perfect, but good enough. It was okay to make mistakes as kids, their feelings mattered and they were able to voice their wants and needs.

Labels for secure attachment style: **confident, balanced, resilient**.

They grow up to have healthy boundaries, a strong sense of self, trust others overall.

They're okay being by themselves.

They're able to connect with others or rely on others for support.

They're flexible thinkers and brainstorm many possibilities to challenges.

They have the emotional resilience to keep going after life's setbacks.

They're comfortable with differences and can resolve conflicts without drama.

They can express their wants and needs to others.

They believe most people are essentially honest and dependable.

They can forgive easily.

Their subconscious thoughts seem to be – *I can have what I want.*

Anxious

Think Piglet.

On the elevator of your nervous system, it's sympathetic (fight or flight).

Anxious attachment styles lived in an inconsistent environment growing up, to the point the child sometimes worried what he or she "did" to cause their parents' behavior. This can be as mild as being raised by a single parent or moving around a lot as a kid, to more extreme cases of neglect or abuse. It's a broad spectrum.

Labels for anxious attachment style: **oversensitive, clingy, needy, emotional, people-pleasers**.

They tend to think about their relationships (personal and professional) a lot.

They worry others do not respect/like/support/love them (depending on the situation).

They're great at nurturing others, but struggle to do so for themselves.

They worry about pleasing others.

They're very attuned to the moods of others.

They struggle with being alone.

If others act differently or are upset, they wonder what they did wrong.

Professionally, they get attached to their staff or clients, and worry they'll leave.

When life changes slightly, that activates their anxiety.

They tend to be prone to drama (some real and some invented). These stressors can come across to varying degrees of neediness, possessiveness, jealousy, control, mood swings, oversensitivity, overthinking.

They excel at working with others, but often doubt themselves the entire way.

Their subconscious thoughts seem to be – *I can want, but I cannot have.*

Avoidant

Think Eeyore.

On the elevator of your nervous system, it's dorsal (freeze or shutdown).

The avoidant attachment style had parents who were emotionally or physically unavailable, either on a minor level or to extreme neglect or abuse. This can be anything as mild as dad and mom worked full-time and had busy social calendars, so there wasn't much family time or one-on-one time, to much more dire situations. Again, this can be a broad spectrum.

Labels for avoidant attachment style: **independent, detached, a loner, insensitive, aloof,   dismissive, cold**.

They're very independent and self-sufficient. They bounce back easily and can put people out of their mind, no problem.

They avoid true emotional intimacy and vulnerability.

They struggle to emotionally support others, even those they care about because it feels draining. They're uncomfortable with others depending on them.

They struggle to connect, work with or rely on others.

Professionally, they prefer to work alone.

Workwise, it's easier to keep finding new clients, rather than nurture current staff or clients.

They may be workaholics, or put outside interests in front of people (hobbies, sports, etc.)

They judge others for not being more self-sufficient and find overly emotional or dramatic people annoying.

Their subconscious thoughts seem to be – *I cannot have, so I do not want.*

Disorganized

This has nothing to do with how nice, neat and tidy you keep your home or car, and everything to do how disorganized attachment styles both wants and fears connection with others. This happens when the parent(s) are both a source of love and fear or distress.

That explains my childhood, since I never knew which dad was walking through the door at home – loving fun, moody, or angry. You can definitely come from a "nice" family, yet still be anxious, avoidant or disorganized for that matter.

Some people lean toward anxious, living in high stress, panicky or rageful states, while others are more disconnected or even shut down, which are more avoidant traits.

Disorganized style is also where extreme cases of childhood abuse and neglect take place. Because of that, this pattern may contribute to addiction, psychiatric conditions, personality disorders or criminal behaviors as adults.

Disorganized attachment styles are described: **adaptable, chameleons**.

They are a combination of both anxious and avoidant styles.

They're highly adaptable because the rules were always changing growing up.

They have a lot of inner conflict.

Their subconscious thoughts seem to be – *I'm not sure what I want, so I probably cannot have.*

If you found characteristic in both anxious and avoidant, chances are you're the disorganized attachment style.

Fear not! No matter your overall attachment style, we can learn to handle whatever life throws our way. We just need to start accessing more ventral in our nervous system to feel more connected to ourselves and others.

Illustration 5

© 2020 Marcy McKay. Graphics – McCollum, R. Adapted from Porges, S.W., Dana, D., Poole Heller, D. & Kipp, M.

Your Attachment Styles Vary

You can have a secure marriage, yet be anxious with your certain coworkers, avoidant with your demanding boss and disorganized with money.

Let's say you're self-employed, you might feel anxious with your clients (therefore, you take great care of them), but you're avoidant about posting consistently on social media and reaching out to potential clients (if that's how you advertise), then completely disorganized with following through on your strategic plan. In fact, you don't have a strategic plan. You're pretty much just winging it.

As the world reopens, you'll never be bored again waiting in lines because you'll have a blast playing *What's their Attachment Style?* It makes for great people watching.

Attachment Combos are Endless

The first time my husband and I learned about attachment styles, we thought I was anxious and he's avoidant. Now that we understand these concepts better we agree that I'm more disorganized-anxious, while Mark is more disorganized-avoidant.

Here's an even funner fact. Depending on the issue in our marriage, we switch between who is more anxious and who is more avoidant.

Isn't that a delicious recipe for power struggles?

This newfound knowledge transformed our relationship more since 2019 than since our wedding in 1990. We've both worked hard to change the stress patterns in our marriage. That alone made our fire worth it.

I never thought I'd write those words, but it's true.

Attachment Disorders

Some say attachment styles not only affects our stress patterns, but also disorders. If you dislike a diagnosis you've received (ADD, ADHD, bipolar disorder, PTSD, depression), or feel your medication is not helping, or feel your disorder has become your identity, consider following those who think outside the box: Dr. Nicole LaPera or Deepak Chopra.

Many thought leaders believe that "disorders" are actually your body's response to traumatic stress. Wise responses trying to get your attention, and not some random label. That you are more than a diagnosis.

Secure Attachment is Always Available

Nobody had a perfect childhood. Over time, we can all learn to feel, think and act in healthier ways. It's never too late to change.

If you're willing to do the work, there's always hope.

Do This!

Four Attachment Styles: Secure. Anxious. Avoidant. Disorganized.

In looking at the different areas of your life, which attachment style are you?

Romance:

Family:

Friends:

Spirituality/Religion:

Career/Business:

Finances:

Health and Fitness:

Fun/Recreation/Play:

Where do you struggle most and why?

_____

_____

_____

Notes

1. Bowlby, J. (1969). Attachment: Attachment and Loss Volume 1: Loss. Basic Books.
2. Heller, D. P. (2019). The power of attachment: how to create deep and lasting intimate relationships. Sounds True.

PART IV
YOUR STRESS BLUEPRINT

13. Your Top 3 Struggles

I was 52 years old before I truly felt consistently calm on a daily basis, even though I was a happy kid, did well in school, had plenty of friends, all my teachers liked me. I was never a great athlete, but my coaches always appreciated my effort and I liked being part of a team. Overall, my school days and childhood were positive.

Outwardly, I had everything as an adult: a loving husband, two great kids, enjoyed many rewarding jobs over the years and volunteer work that fulfilled me. I've written two award-winning novels. I'm fully aware I've experienced much more joy than heartache.

However, even before the fire, I already knew on a gut-level my three biggest struggles were:

1. Perfectionism.
2. Care-taking.
3. Guilt (not good enough).

Those three combined together were an abusive cocktail I drank on a regular basis. I want to explain more of my backstory to help you pinpoint your Top 3 Struggles.

I subconsciously shamed myself that I didn't respond *perfectly* during our house fire. I didn't call 911 *immediately*, or even after my husband told me to. I waited a full 133 seconds after the alarm sounded before doing the *right thing*.

That sounds almost silly if you're not a perfectionist, you just might think *no biggie. You still did it. Get over yourself, girl.*

Intellectually, I understood the fire was not my fault, and said so out loud, but the rational part of my brain wasn't in charge of my perfectionism and other go-to strategies. This was deep and purely irrational. These were the thoughts beneath my thoughts. My insides subconsciously screamed:

WE LOST OUR HOUSE ON MYYYYYYYYYYYYYY WATCH!

This triggered my *perfectionism* button so hard that I beat myself up with my oldest tormenter – *guilt. Never good enough* had been part of my internal hardwiring for as long as I can remember.

Nicole's Top 3 Struggles

She's the successful commercial banker who grew up poor with her mentally-ill mom and sweet, but her overwhelmed dad. Nicole's Top 3 Struggles were:

1. Shame.
2. People-pleasing.
3. Self-Doubt.

Despite putting herself through college on her own, having a thriving marriage and career, Nicole still felt somehow less than everyone else because of her childhood.

The workplace is built on relationships, so it can be as

dysfunctional as any family barbeque. She often over-gave or ignored her own needs and boundaries.

Nicole and one of her overbearing coworkers were on the same client projects together a lot, but he wouldn't do his part. This stalled everything, which meant they would lose the account, anger the client, or somehow not get paid. Frustrated, Nicole often did his job for him, which became an unspoken pattern of theirs for years.

No more.

She did not walk into the office one day with her guns a blazin' (remember, she lives in Texas, y'all). Nicole did not lecture him on his mistreatment. Instead, she stayed calm when he "told her" to do something that was his responsibility. She refused and "told him" to do it himself.

Guess what?

He did it.

Her confidence grew as she stood up to him each time, and started calling out his BS more often. This did not happen all at once, but Nicole changed in baby steps.

Was there pushback?

Sometimes, yes.

Sometimes, no.

Either way, Nicole learned that she survived. She didn't melt from his anger. She didn't lose his respect. She didn't die. She even told a superior who actually listened about her co-worker's laziness and that helped tremendously.

In fact, their partnership is better than ever because now it's built on mutual respect. She did not do any of this perfectly, and still sometimes slides back into old behaviors. When her physical-and/or-emotional pain returns, Nicole remembers her self-worth and gets back on track.

She doesn't flounder as long.

Your Body is Responding Perfectly

Your stress is real. Your body is responding perfectly to *your* old patterns, as uncomfortable as they may be. Plus, the more people in your inner circle, then the more mixed feelings you may be experiencing. Everyone's nervous systems are bumping up against each other during these trying times.

What are your Top 3 Struggles? Pick what's causing you the most distress right now.

_____

_____

_____

Do This!

Even if you scored 5 on every single item on Today's Emotions/Behaviors Assessment (Chapter 7), please narrow your list now. What are your Top 3 Struggles? And, how are they showing up in your life today?

1.

2.

3.

How did these 3 Struggles show up in your life before 2020? Be as specific as you can.

1.

2.

3.

Where do you think these 3 originated?

_____

_____

_____

14. Your Snapshot Moments

When I think of me growing up as Susie Sunshine, it's always the same mental picture. What I'm about to share did not really happen, it's how I felt playing that childhood role. I picture my dad (all 6' 3" and 300-pounds of him) standing in the center of our living room, with that groovy, 1970s lime-green shag carpet we had in our house. Of course, that's where he stood because he was the center of my universe.

I'm spinning around him as fast I can like the Tasmanian Devil. Spinning, spinning – doing my best to keep him happy. I'm different ages as I spin, depending on how old I feel in the memory – I'm five, ten, maybe fifteen. The age doesn't matter, I'm always spinning.

The problem was, his rules were always changing, so no matter how hard I tried, it somehow wasn't good enough. I could not anticipate his mood changes fast enough to keep the peace and could never stay one step ahead of him. His rage was terrifying.

This is where Susie Sunshine was born. Intellectually, I see how unrealistic this is because I was just a kid. Nobody is happy all the time – plus, my dad worked hard to take care of our family, but this was still a lifelong pattern that in order for me to be okay, I had to make him okay first.

That's not okay.

Your Invisible Lens of the World

Our lives are made of moments. Tiny snapshots of the highs and the lows, the joys and heartbreaks we've all faced like a Polaroid picture that spits out a camera photo you watch develop before your very eyes.

Your nervous system is the sum total of all your lived experiences. Let's pretend I line up three people and give each one special X-Ray glasses that affect how they see the world.

Person #1 wears ventral glasses (connected). She views most everyone and everything in a positive and realistic light. Nobody is perfect, but she generally sees the good in all and can brainstorm solutions for the difficulties that come her way.

Person #2 wears sympathetic glasses (fight or flight). He sees the world anywhere from anxious and panicky, to irrational and out of control. He struggles to make decisions on his own, or might seem unsure of himself and look to others for validation. Maybe, he's great in a crisis, but drama somehow seems to follow him, as if the sky is always falling. Or, he feels he must fix the problem or save the day right now. Sometimes, when he gets mad, it gets ugly. There are many variations to sympathetic.

Person #3 wears dorsal glasses (freeze or shutdown). There's a wide range to her spectrum, too. She can be anywhere from sarcastic and grumpy, to pessimistic pretty much all the time. Maybe she's just in a downer mood, or she might be full-blown depressed and isolating to the point that her family and friends are concerned about her well-being. Maybe she's all smiles on the outside, but inside – she's numb or shutdown.

Each emotional state has so many varying degrees because no two people have the exact shared history, even within the same family. Your stressors may share commonalities with others, but your anxiety is unique to you alone, like a thumbprint. Therefore, you must create the right thoughts and habits that work for your nervous system

Your Snapshot Moment(s)

We all experience life through our own invisible lens of the world. Most of us don't realize it's even there because it's happening at the subconscious level, the thoughts beneath your thoughts.

That's your nervous system in action.

Therapy, church, yoga, meditation, exercise, inspiring podcasts are all wonderful tools, so please continue to do anything that is a positive in your life. However, your brain still sees certain thoughts, behaviors or goals you want to change, but are struggling with as UNSAFE.

Your nervous system continues to carry those stressful moments from the past inside you like invisible snapshots – almost like your own personal Viewfinder. That cool toy where you could trade out the different cardboard reels of pictures that told a story.

You've never experienced a global pandemic before, but your nervous system instinctively recognizes the unknown as scary. If your narcissistic mom always made you feel unworthy, it might explain why everything about quarantine life feels torturous to you.

If your brother died when you were six, but your family

never dealt with the loss, that unresolved grief might be resurfacing now.

If your dad was always off at work and your mom was always gone volunteering, it's reasonable that you've carried that abandonment through the years.

Find Your Snapshot Moment

Think back to your Top 3 Struggles. Often, they're closely related to your snapshot moment, which came from your stress origins (Chapter 4). This is where your patterns began, the coping strategies that made you who you are today – the good, the bad and the ugly. Your thoughts, beliefs and behaviors.

In psychological terms, this is your root cause. Your root cause might be a one-time event, such as when your family lost everything and you had to move in with your grandparents.

Or, you might not have a clear image. Your stressors might have been ongoing part of your life like living with your mom's undiagnosed depression. I wish I could give you an exact formula, but trauma doesn't work that way.

Do not panic if you do not have a clear image yet. It may come to you in time, just go with whatever you're thinking or feeling right now, even if it's not directly related to what I've said.

Trust your instincts. This can be challenging because these struggles are often connected to painful memories. Remember the statistics from Dr. Bessel van der Kolk:

One in five Americans was sexually molested as a child.

One in four was beaten by a parent to the point of a mark left on their body.

One in three couples engages in physical violence.

One-quarter of us grew up with alcoholic relatives.

One out of eight people witnessed their mother being beaten or hit.

Trauma is so much more common than we realize, so please do not feel ashamed. Shame is a poison that keeps us feeling hurt, broken and damaged. Shame keeps us isolated and alone. However, they are the invisible sunglasses that affect how you see the world. These are the patterns you've been wanting to change.

Some of you will have concrete memories for your snapshot moment because these events truly occurred in your life. Other people, like me, do not picture actual memories, but more so have images that represent certain feelings from the past.

There is no right or wrong here.

Susie Sunshine encompasses my Top 3 Struggles of perfectionism, people-pleasing, and guilt (feeling never good enough). Here is another example of mine where it probably all began.

Marcy's Snapshot – The Plane Crash

This moment plays through my mind more like an old home movie than an actual photograph. It really happened to my father, but I was so young I don't recall it per se, yet I still somehow remember all the chaotic feelings. It's fine if you don't believe that is possible because I sometimes doubt it, too.

In the fall of 1968, I was two years old, my older brother was five, and our younger sister wasn't born yet. Our dad was the sole survivor of a private plane crash when he was thirty-four. The two other men on board died that day.

I feel the frantic energy from all the grownups around me – my mom, my grandparents, all our family friends. Everyone's initial shock and horror. Their panic, their terror. Was Roy dead or alive? Then, the days and weeks that followed while he was hospitalized. Would he walk again? What would happen to our family?

Again, this isn't The Blame Game. As an adult, I fully understand how that crisis changed my dad forever – his boss and coworker died beside him and he could not save them. It crushed his vertebrae and made him a full inch shorter afterwards. A plane crash is trauma with a capital "T."

However, this happened when I was a mere toddler. I did not have the words or capacity to process that crisis. I just absorbed everyone's stress like a sponge.

Two-year-old Me just did her best to make Daddy happy again, which set up that lifelong pattern. His opinion was everything. That coping strategy varied as a I grew older, depending on the environment and the situation: to my family, teachers, certain friends, my bosses, various coworkers, to my husband.

The people were interchangeable, but the pattern was set.

It's Susie Sunshine's job to *please* you, or fix this *perfectly*. Anything else was *not good enough* and left her feeling like a failure. These were the sunglasses in which I unknowingly saw the world.

Do you see now why the house fire sparked my unhealed trauma?

Eli's Story:

Other people have concrete memories that are their snapshot moments. Eli came to me as he approached his 50th birthday. His second marriage was failing, even though they had two kids that he and his wife both adored. Eli still loved her, but worried she was drinking again.

His Top 3 Struggles were:

1. Shame.
2. Sexual abuse.
3. Feeling unworthy.

Eli's Snapshot #1 – Dead or Alive?

Eli can picture himself panicked as a young boy (around age six), watching his alcoholic mom passed out on the couch. He could not wake her and thought she had died. This happened often over the years, but that one moment sums up all the terror he unknowingly carried for decades. It was the sunglasses in which he saw the world and explained why he always felt he had to rescue people, personally and professionally.

His first wife had been an alcoholic, too. He kept choosing his mom over and over in different ways, trying (and failing) to save her.

Eli's Snapshot #2 – The Dark Place

His second Polaroid moment was being molested from the ages of nine to eleven by a neighborhood widower who all the parents loved on their block. Eli remembers one particular afternoon in that basement that encompasses so much of his shame.

Both snapshots explain Eli's feelings of unworthiness, his constant struggle with self-doubt, always choosing the wrong women and his inability to focus or follow-through with personal goals – despite having a thriving business.

Eli tackled his shame and unworthiness head on. Turns out, his wife was drinking again, but she agreed to go to treatment. He really focused on his own healing, as well as supporting his children's worries and fears over their mom. Their whole family began to change. Eli is still evolving, but he feels more confident than ever because his past is no longer controlling him.

Can't Think of a Snapshot Moment?

It's okay. Seriously. Maybe instead of a specific memory – you feel a certain emotion, see a color, or feel a physical sense in your body. Do not panic and feel like you're not "doing this right."

It's more important to pay attention to your current stress symptoms – fear, sadness, anger, guilt, self-doubt, procrastination, your obsessive-compulsive tendencies, your struggle to focus, or however anxiety is showing up for you today.

Where are you on your nervous system elevator?

The fact that you feel dysregulated, in sympathetic (fight or flight) or dorsal (freeze or shutdown) is more critical at the moment than any specific memory.

Do This!

List your Top 3 Struggles:

1.

2.

3.

Now, think of 2 – 3 Snapshot Moments that illustrate these struggles. These are visual representations of your stress origins (Chapter 4). They might be actual events from your life, or just reflect certain feelings.

If something else comes to mind other than what I've said, trust your intuition and go with that. Just write.

_____

_____

_____

_____

_____

_____

15. Critical Voices

In addition to the snapshot moments (Chapter 14) that represent your Top 3 Struggles (Chapter 13), there also tends to be at least one critical voice subconsciously playing inside your head. A disapproving grinch who has been there so long that you may not even notice him or her. These are more of those thoughts beneath your thoughts, desperate to keep the status quo in your life, even if that straight-up sucks for you.

It's your nervous system screaming UNSAFE and wanting to keep you stuck.

Bleh.

Sometimes, the critical voice connects directly to your snapshot moment, letting you know all the ways you're falling short. I began making a list of the critical voices in 1996 as clients mentioned different struggles to me. It's always easier to spot the patterns in others.

Since perfectionism, people-pleasing and guilt were my three biggest struggles, it makes sense that my two loudest Critical Voices are:

1. *I'm not good enough.*
2. *I'm bad.*

Nobody ever said those actual words to me, but those were the messages I received and the voices change internally, depending on the situation.

"I'm not good enough" is the loudest one, but if I do make

a mistake or get triggered with shame, it becomes, "I'm bad."

In fact, my mom commented a few years ago that she and my dad never had to punish me like they did my brother or sister growing up. My parents just said, "They were so disappointed in me," then I took care of the rest.

Other Critical Voices

I told you about my writer friend Jay who had throat cancer. *"It doesn't matter,"* was his loudest critical voice. That was part of why he couldn't get started on his novel. Why bother to write anything when nothing he said or did mattered?

Eli had the alcoholic mom. His loudest critical voice was, *"I'm not lovable."* He felt his mother loved the bottle more than him, then the sexual abuse seemed to prove his unworthiness even more.

Rachel's narcissistic mom's loudest voice confirmed her worst fear, *"I don't belong."* She didn't fit in with her own family or her first husband, and that loneliness followed her for years.

Nicole said her critical voice is, *"I'm a fraud."* Despite her happy marriage, and successful career, she was still that poor girl and always worried people would find out and learn the truth and somehow kick her out of life.

How about you?

What are the Critical Voices inside your head saying to you? Even if no one said the actual damaging words to you, it's the way you *feel*.

Do This!

Take the Critical Voice Assessment to find out which negative voice is triggering your nervous system the most.

My Book Accelerator course, *Transform Your Stress*, has all the book's exercises and assessments together in one workbook, as well as 3.5 hours worth of bonus video content:

https://marcymckay.teachable.com/p/transform-your-stress/.

STRESS ASSESSMENT - CRITICAL VOICES

Pretend you're 10 years old or younger, still living in your childhood home. Circle as many of these *messages* that resonate with you (even if no one ever said these actual words to you.)

Please note you might have more than one critical voice for different situations.

I'm Not (good) Enough.	I'm a Failure.
I'm Invisible.	I'm Not Normal (too different).
I'm Bad.	I Don't Belong.
I'm a Fraud/Phony.	I Don't Have.
I'm Alone.	I'm Not Important.
I (my needs) Don't Matter.	I'm Less Than (inferior).
I'm Not Lovable.	I'm Unworthy/Worthless.
I'm Not Wanted.	I'm Wrong.
I'm Not Safe.	I Don't Deserve (happiness,
I'm a Burden.	success, etc.)
I'm Crazy.	What other phrases do you hear?
I'm Too Much.	_____
I'm Powerless.	_____

Which voice is loudest in your head and why?

_____

_____

_____

_____

_____

_____

_____

How young does this critical voice make you feel?

_____

Where do you think you learned this message? Try to be as specific as possible (even if no one said the actual words to you). It can be more than one source (a parent, a critical teacher, a friend, an abusive ex, a coworker).

_____

_____

_____

_____

How is this critical voice showing up in your life today?

_____

_____

_____

_____

16. Stressed Out

Mark and I spent our wedding night in 1990 on Interstate-40 in our hometown of Amarillo, Texas. My in-laws thought it'd be hilarious to book us the honeymoon suite at the famed The Big Texan Ranch. That's where travelers have come from all over the world for over fifty years to eat a 72-ounce steak and all the fixings in less than one hour in order to get their meal for free. It's hokey, kitschy, and touristy. It's also a BOOMING business. They're often packed.

Our room came complete with a cowhide loveseat, swinging saloon doors to the bathroom, and lots of old-timey photos on the walls. We chuckled about it until my husband realized our air conditioner was broken and there was a heatwave that holiday weekend. The entire motel was sold out, so we slept on our comforter on the floor where it was cooler, listening to the eighteen-wheelers roll by and honk all night long.

When we reached our honeymoon tropical destination, the air conditioner was also broken in our first room, too, but the resort moved us to another one right away.

After we returned home one week later to Austin, Texas, where it's *hot* in September – I kid you not, the air conditioner was broken in our little rent house. There was no manager to move us to a new room.

Three different broken air conditioners in three different places over one week. My new husband was dripping with sweat when he said, "You're really nice, but I'm not sure this marriage is going to work."

Do you know what this story illustrates?

Life.

Dividing up the Stress

After the fire, our insurance company offered to set up my family long term at another motel on Interstate-40 near The Big Texan.

Luckily, we rented a house elsewhere. For the past 20 years, we'd been parents to our two kids and had focused nonstop on them, but our son was in his senior year of high school and we'd be empty-nesters when he left for college in a few months. My father-in-law had just moved my mother-in-law into an Alzheimer's unit, so Mark was mired in the grief over losing his mom, without the closure of a funeral.

We had so many other important issues to tend to, but the fire became priority #1 overnight. We already had jobs, which meant twice as much work to do, yet no energy to accomplish anything.

Mark and I played to our strengths. He dealt with insurance and all the endless business matters as we debated on whether or not to move home. I was day-to-day operations and special projects – such as what to do with the hundreds of hangers of our de-smoked clothes that gratefully survived the fire. They couldn't go back into our destroyed house and our rental was too small. I found various folks gracious enough to share their extra space.

My husband and I made an exhausted, but good team. Adulting means constantly dealing with stuff we don't want to do. Tending to the "check engine" light in your car.

Scheduling that doctor's appointment about your back pain.

Letting go of that friendship which no longer serves you.

Stress Patterns

For you – it's not just all the other hot topics on the news right now, but your personal issues on top of everything else. The broken air conditioner, the rift between loved ones over politics, So-and-So needs treatment for her eating disorder now.

Real life happens behind closed doors.

Dr. Harriet Lerner is a clinical psychologist known for her expertise in relationships. In her international bestseller, *The Dance of Anger: A Woman's Guide to Changing the Patterns of Intimate Relationships*, she explains how everyone has patterned ways of managing stress from our first family – childhood. There are basically two types of people – *over*functioners and *under*functioners.[1]

See who you recognize in each group.

*Over*functioners

*Over*functioners are sympathetic (fight or flight). They tend to respond to stress by moving straight into action. They swoop in to save the day. They take charge and take control. They often disregard offers for help, because deep down they worry nobody will do it as well as them.

If they're not handling the situation, they often micromanage, or offer unsolicited advice. They can view others as weak or flaky for not leaping tall buildings in a single bound. They struggle to show their vulnerability, especially with those they consider as having problems.

Negative labels for *over*functioners: bossy, control freaks, know-it-alls.

Rather than feel their feelings, *over*functioners **do** stuff. Their thoughts seem to be – *Gotta fix it now! It's up to me. I'm the only one who can make this better.*

If you guessed that I am an *over*functioner, you would be right.

*Under*functioners

*Under*functioners are dorsal (freeze or shut down). They tend to respond to stress by moving straight into **in**action. They'd rather avoid the situation, so they procrastinate, detach, or retreat altogether. They sometimes become the focus of gossip within the family or workplace because they cannot 'get it together.' Some *under*functioners are considered to be the 'problem child' because they don't play by the group's unspoken rules.

*Under*functioners can view others as overbearing or demanding, but if things go wrong, it's not the *under*functioner's fault. They were not in charge. Often, they struggle to get organized in several areas of life, even developing physical-and-emotional symptoms when stress runs high.

Negative labels for *under*functioners: irresponsible, lazy, unreliable.

Rather than feel their feelings, *under*functioners tend to **do little, or nothing**. Their thoughts seem to be, *I don't know about this. I'm not sure how to fix this, so let's wait and see what happens.*

More Childhood Patterns

Dr. Lerner talks about *over*-and-*under*functioning as patterned responses to anxiety, rather than deep truths to who we are. These patterns often stem from childhood and can be changed.

If you're an *over*functioner, you may not believe that others have much value to you. Practice showing the more tender, vulnerable parts of yourself. Stop sharing all the answers for everyone else. You don't always know what's best. Plus, you rob others of the chance to learn and grow themselves.

*Under*functioners would benefit from doing the exact opposite. Tone down your expressions of vulnerability and amplify your strength and competence, even if you're not sure you can do it.

Lerner says, "Whatever your patterned behaviors may be, you can cultivate a more authentic voice, if you're willing to practice doing what does not come naturally."

Do This!

In responding to stress, do you tend to *over*function, or *under*function?

_____

_____

Once you identify that, look at a stressful situation from your life, then list the actual behaviors that accompany your *over/under*functioning.

_____

_____

_____

Notes

1. Lerner, H. G. (1985). The dance of anger: a woman's guide to changing the patterns of intimate relationships. Avon.

17. Connecting the Dots

I was away at college when my first IT happened, changing me forever. Long before cell phones existed, my father would call multiple times a week to share about the weather back home, or remind me to change the oil in my car, or make sure I had a full tank of gas. Some of you will think that is overbearing, while others will find it endearing.

You'd both be right.

Since Dad traveled a lot, if he was within a 200-mile radius of Waco, Texas, then he was "in the neighborhood" and would swing to visit me at Baylor University. My father always held court in my apartment. All my roommates and friends adored him and stopped by to experience his charm, his jokes, and his advice that they gobbled up like candy.

Roy Mason was an EVENT.

Afterwards, he took me and a childhood friend (he had nicknamed us Heckle and Jeckle as kids) to his favorite dive honky-tonk for the best steaks in town. After we dropped her off, the two of us grabbed Baskin Robbins ice cream like we did all those years ago. I had *fun dad* for the evening, so I took full advantage of it. We went back his hotel to eat and hang out.

I ate one scoop of chocolate, while he polished off an entire quart of Rocky Road, then made me promise not to tell my mother. For the next two hours, we talked about anything and everything: how school was going, what I wanted to do with my life, who he thought I would marry (my husband was one of the three guys he predicted and we weren't even dating at the time). My dad asked my opinion on different topics, then *listened*.

That was new. Typically, I spent the night at my parents' hotel to get a break from college, but I didn't for the first time because I had a 9 o'clock study group and left. Pride swelled within me as I drove away because he'd never treated me like an adult before. I thought we had turned the corner in our relationship.

Instead, we were saying goodbye.

My father had a heart attack and died alone in his hotel room.

That was April 2, 1987. He was fifty-two years old. My mom became a widow at the age of forty-four. My brother was twenty-three, I was twenty, my sister was just fifteen. It blindsided our family.

Here I was, Susie Sunshine, the girl who'd spent a lifetime trying to please her father, hungry to make him okay, so she could be okay ...

He died on *my watch*.

Thirty years later, we lost our family home on *my watch*.

BOOM.

THAT is what unraveled me. That is why the house fire brought me to my knees and brought up so many unhealed wounds from the past. That stress had stayed stored in my body for decades. Nobody blamed me for either event, and, intellectually, I agreed.

But subconsciously – it was a whole different story. I blamed me. To my nervous system, I had failed my childhood family in the worst way possible with my father's death, only to commit the same unforgivable sin thirty years later with my own family and the fire.

The truth hit me so hard that it cut me to my core. It also explained my people-pleasing over the years. **You** *will die if I do not fix you and your problems +* **I** *will die if I do not fix you and your problems.*

This was the missing piece of my internal puzzle that explained EVERYTHING. Why our house fire in 2017 triggered me so badly, why it unleashed so much physical-and-emotional pain, as well as why I'd had all those coping strategies since childhood. I finally understood what snapped inside me.

Connecting the dots does not have to be a direct correlation. I had never been through a fire before, and most of you have never experienced a global pandemic either, yet you still feel unsettled, anxious, stressed and out of sorts.

It also doesn't have to be rational. In fact, the more irrational it is, the more you say *this is ridiculous, but*, or *this sounds silly or crazy, but* … you're absolutely on the right track. Follow that thought, no matter how bizarre it seems.

Roy Mason – A Case Study

My father was on a work trip when IT happened for him. He boarded his boss's private plane with one other salesman and they headed out for the day. The three would be home by dinner.

The engine failed and the plane crashed about thirty miles outside of Odessa, Texas. Upon impact, my dad gripped his armrests and saw through his tiny window how the sand shot up into the air.

He began walking towards a white light, but wasn't afraid. In fact, he felt drawn to the light because of its incredible beauty. Dad was about to step into the whiteness when he noticed two small figures making their way across a field of flowers to him.

He waited.

The pair held hands – it was me and my brother, Greg. When we reached him, I said, "Come on Daddy, let's go home."

He took our hands and we left.

When my father opened his eyes, the sand was just settling back to ground.

Had it been a split second, a lifetime, or both?

I never heard my father talk about that plane crash. Not once in the twenty years he was in my life.

Curious people would ask him about it since not many have survived such an ordeal, but he would either change the subject with a funny remark, or shut them down cold for asking such a personal question – depending on his mood in that nanosecond.

I didn't understand back then that he had PTSD. My father struggled with massive survivor's guilt. Why had he lived, while the other two men died? Both were family men, well respected in their community. It made no sense. Talking about the plane crash triggered his trauma, so of course, he avoided the topic since he had so much unresolved pain.

I think my dad hurt every day after for the rest of his life, both physically and emotionally.

I only knew the private details of the crash because my mom mentioned it after letting me read her copy of *Angels: God's Secret Agents* by Billy Graham when I was nine. We talked about it and I asked her a bazillion questions.

What? Not every third grader is preoccupied with near-death experiences?

Hmmm, go figure.

The plane crash doesn't even include connecting the dots back to my father's childhood. I'm sure he thought he'd long since left that unhappiness behind from his alcoholic dad because he'd created a better family with us, but his stress patterns had been set.

He did his best to squash his pain with cigarettes, food and funny stories, but his feelings erupted in other destructive ways.

My family got caught in the crossfire.

Everyone Has a Light and Dark Side

Almost 20 years after my father died, my brother returned to Dad's tiny hometown in Central Texas for the funeral of my dad's childhood best friend. The man had been Greg's godfather, so I'm sure attending the service felt more like a family funeral.

Afterwards, people swarmed my brother once they realized that he was "Roy Garner's son" (Garner was my dad's middle name and what everyone called him growing up). Plus, my father has a fan club almost everywhere on the planet.

Woman #1 told my brother, "Your daddy taught me how to ride a bike."

Woman #2 giggled. "Your daddy taught me how to swim."

Woman #2 winked. "Your daddy taught me how to drink beer."

My brother just laughed. "Ladies, Roy Garner taught me how to do all three."

Whether it's your parents, your lover, your sister or your best friend, nobody is perfect. Most everyone has a light side and dark side. It's just easier to spot and appreciate in some than in others.

Yes, some people are total jack-wagons, but most aren't.

Your Stress Symptoms Matter Most

The same is true for your coping strategies now. They're probably repeating in more than one area right now – stopping you from living your best life, even before 2020. If you cannot fully remember how your past all fits together with your coping strategies right now, that's okay.

It takes time.

Truly.

As I've said before, it's more important to pay attention to your stress symptoms. If you feel dysregulated – in sympathetic (fight or flight) or dorsal (freeze or shut down) – that is all that matters. Learn how to feel more regulated, more connected and to enjoy longer periods in ventral. The rest will come in due time.

Do This!

Journal about what insights come to mind about your stress patterns and how they connect to your past. I don't want to put pressure on you because this is challenging work emotionally.

_____

_____

_____

_____

_____

_____

_____

_____

Spend some time trying to connect the dots to your

parents, your romantic partner – even if you don't know their full backstory.

_____

_____

_____

_____

_____

_____

_____

_____

18. Putting out the Fire

I'm home alone as I write once again, but the world feels so much different this time. A global pandemic still ravages the entire planet, and we have no idea what the new normal will look like.

We're all watching this unfold together.

On mornings when I wake up to that familiar aNxIeTy, I remind myself that my nervous system has never been through anything like this, so, *of course*, I feel stressed. I've simply fallen back into old patterns.

Most of the time, I'm able to inch my way up my personal elevator from sympathetic into ventral, then enjoy my day. Or, at least not feel quite so distressed.

When I cannot seem to swing that and feel stuck, lost or hopeless, then I try to remind myself that my dorsal-ness won't last forever. It still panics me at first and triggers my critical voice I'm somehow doing this all "wrong" or that "I'm bad", but I remember to reach out to friends in ways I didn't before.

The good news is that my bounce back time is so much faster and better is better.

My family still juggles financial worries, health concerns, communication breakdowns and all the other behind-the-scene issues with our families, or people we love like family. I'm also prone to many *WTH* moments because –

well, that's just me. I may not be tall like my father (I'm 5'4"), but I carry BIG emotions just like him.

It's a blessing and a curse.

What's changed most in my life since the fire is absolutely everything.

Far more than where we live, I'm so much happier as a person. I'm calmer, more at peace, and feel more resilient when the sh*t hits the fan because that what sh*t does.

It hits the fan.

Nobody has a perfect life.

Yes, and ...

Healing Your Trauma

Just as there is *not one size fits all* for explaining your stress patterns, the same is true for overcoming your emotional blocks, childhood wounds, trauma – whatever you want to call it.

Remember, everybody has emotional trauma, so there's nothing to be ashamed of – stop believing how shiny everyone else's lives seem.

I'm about to share my Top 12 Tips.

Everything on this list is part of my personal routine. I'd like to say I do them all daily, but life also requires that I work, cook, clean, eat, do laundry, and deal with *stuff*, so some tips are more weekly, or as needed.

Being flexible is the sign of a more flexible nervous system.

Yes, amnesia still hits me and I forget to do these tips, or I think I'm somehow magically better and don't need them anymore, or I flat-out resist because I don't #$%@ want to that day.

Then, my physical and/or emotional pain returns and I get back to work. My joy, curiosity and compassion all return. It works like magic.

Lovingly getting back on track after mistakes, setbacks, U-turns or failures may be my biggest lesson of all because they're absolutely part of the process.

One topic is not more important than the other because they're all interconnected. Remember, there is no mind-body connection – you're one being.

What happens to one part of you affects every part of you.

1. Your Overall Health Matters

I always feel empowered when I focus on what I can control, which is paramount since so much feels topsy-turvy these days. When I make progress, or see change in others whom I admire or respect, that encourages me to keep going and to keep growing.

Sleep – If you're struggling at all in this department, read *Sleep Smarter: 21 Essential Strategies to Sleep Your Way to a Better Body, Better Health and Bigger Success* by Shawn Stevenson.[1] I discovered this wonderful book in 2017 a few months before our house fire since my insomnia, hormone problems and weight gain were already problems. The book is so conversational and easy to understand, covering everything from health, to supplements, to getting a better night's rest. It even offers a 14-Day Sleep Makeover.

Your Gut Health – You can heal all of your emotional trauma, but if you're eating meals from a To-Go bag or a box, then you will still feel like crap. Junk food causes inflammation, which causes stress to your muscles, joints and brain. It's all interconnected. Eat better to feel better.

Food Matters – Avoid carbohydrates and sugary foods (that includes alcohol). This one is tough because I cannot even count how many times I've fallen off the carb wagon since 2020. Food is definitely one of the ways that I self-soothe (another pattern I learned from my dad because eating was one of his love languages). I'm working on it.

Rather than three big meals per day, eat smaller, well-balanced meals, about every three to four hours. Eat plenty of omega-3 fats to give your mood a boost, like salmon, walnuts, and flaxseeds. If this sounds like I'm speaking a foreign language, read *Sleep Smarter*.

Stress Drinking – The Associated Press reported in March 2020 that the purchase of alcohol in the U.S. has increased 55% since March 2019. Spirits like tequila, gin and pre-mixed cocktails were highest with a 75% increase, while wine sales were up 66%, and beer rose 42%. Online sales of alcohol were up a staggering 243%.[2]

I realize alcohol helps numb the pain, which we've all needed while quarantining, but alcohol is also a depressant and the sugar stresses out your body more. That makes you feel even worse, so you pour another drink, creating a vicious cycle.

This is the one tip I get the most pushback on, but here's the truth. Alcohol exacerbates feelings of anxiety, depression and isolation. It makes your life so much more difficult. Lose the booze, or at least drink less.

If alcohol has become an addiction, please consider finding a treatment center for help. You and your loved ones deserve you at your very best.

Limit Your Screen Time – I do not know anyone who has said, *OMG! I am SO GLAD I've watched endless conspiracy-theory videos about every topic, AND the 24-hour news cycle, AND vaccinations! It makes me feel SO MUCH BETTER that I want to hang out ALL DAY on social media to argue with family and friends!*

You see where I'm going. Not only does it matter what you feed your body, it also matters what you feed your brain. Do not keep the TV on all day or your laptop playing, even if it's fun rom-coms that you have on simply for background noise.

It's too much. Your mind needs breathing room. A chance to think new thoughts, solve problems, ponder, dream, create. Shut off all technology at least one hour before bedtime.

Journal – Everything else on #1 deals with input, while journaling is output. Our survival brain likes to churn nonstop. Replaying past hurts, worrying about the future, staying stuck in a loop of negativity like a hamster wheel spinning, but going nowhere fast.

Journaling moves those incessant thoughts from your head, onto the page and begins to quiet your mind over time. The more I complain about the same topic, the more my brain tires of my whining, then either focuses on acceptance or a solution. I think of journaling as a Brain Drain. For this kind of journaling, I do not recommend using a pretty little journal because I feel pressured to write pretty little thoughts. I use a big ol' 3-or-5 subject notebook like I used in high school, so I can dump my thoughts, feelings, frustrations, ideas, inspirations – everything onto the page.

I write by hand three pages as fast as I can, just stream of consciousness. I write BIG and LOOPY, almost illegible. The first page is usually just me griping about my current problems, like a laundry list of complaints. On page 2, I usually have a post-it on there from the previous day with a question that I'm pondering. By page 3, I'm usually calmer, or at least – less anxious. I've done this practice for almost 25 years.

I prefer journaling by hand over typing at the computer, but do what works best for you.

Keep Reaching into Your Stress Busters Toolbox – This helps get you reconnected to yourself and others when (not if) you're trapped in fight-flight-freeze. Make a concrete, go-to list for self-care. I keep mine on my phone to access at any time.

2. Move Your Body

Exercise is a great way to relieve stress. Since my home away from home is sympathetic, I need to exercise to get rid of excess energy. You might be more dorsal and need to move out of your numbness, which I understand is absolutely the hardest time to do it.

Just do your best.

You don't have to go hardcore and lift weights (even though it's great for you). Plus, gyms are opening and closing daily. I like to walk, jog, or hike outside in nature, but that may not be your choice. Or, you might be in lockdown in your area and unable to leave home.

If that's the case, crank up the music and dance around to your favorite tunes. Do jumping jacks, squats, sit-ups or pushups. Use resistance bands.

There are endless free workout videos online for strength training, yoga, or whatever fitness interests you. Some people want and need to pay for online memberships or classes to show up, to feel better, or best of all – to be part of a community and to find a new tribe. That's terrific since both self-regulation and co-regulation are part of our healing journey.

Be creative.

Find something you enjoy and stick with it, but don't be afraid to try new activities. Early in 2020, my husband found a punching bag for dirt cheap at a secondhand store that he set up in our garage to punch, kick and go all ninja on that thing. It's become one of his go-to workouts.

Breaking a sweat for just five minutes improves your stress levels a lot.

The **Brain Savvy** app (discussed in Chapter 8) helps me pay attention to the behaviors I can control, how to keep a more positive mindset and how my progress is going (currently, I'm struggling sleeping with insomnia). The app is an easy reminder that small changes in my daily habits makes a big difference.

3. Let the Sunshine In

This is one of my favorite hacks because it's so simple

and free. Vitamin D is a natural mood booster. Sunshine lifts your spirts, relaxes you, and strengthens your focus. If that's not reason enough to get you outside, sunshine resets your circadian rhythms and helps you sleep better and even lose weight.[3]

Set down your phone and sit, stand or walk outside for 5 – 20 minutes. For those worried about skin cancer, go outside in the morning before the sun hits the hottest part of the day.

If you cannot get outside, or the weather is dreary where you are, then buy a Vitamin D lamp. We have one at home and just bought one online for $39.99 to send to our son at college. I think they are worth the investment.

Yes, you can take Vitamin D supplements, but the real deal is so much better.

4. Grounding

This may sound straight-up wackadoodle, but it makes me feel so much better that I became a believer after our fire.

"Grounding" or sometimes called "earthing" helps turn off the fight-flight-freeze when your nervous system feels activated. It grounds you back into your body and into the present moment.[4]

Simply go outside and stand or walk barefoot in the grass, dirt, sand, or ground because the earth has an endless supply of negative electrons. Again, ditch your phone while you do this. I'm not Alexander Graham Bell, but I know a phone is an electrical system. You don't want to be holding one electrical system while you're trying to calm your body's internal electrical system.

Do this for 5 to 20 minutes, whatever time you have. This can also be your Vitamin D time.

Grounding if You Cannot Go Outside

Here are some alternatives if you don't have time, or the weather is not cooperating or your area is in lockdown:

Give yourself a footbath – Fill up your tub or a bucket of warm water. Add Epsom salt, herbs or essential oils and soak for 10 minutes. Put your phone away and just pamper yourself.

Window bathing – If the sun is shining, sit by a window (open it if you can and weather permitting) and soak up the Vitamin D that way.

Listen to nature sounds or music – You can find these sounds online for free: the ocean, the breeze, a thunderstorm or more. Whatever parts of nature appeals to your senses.

Five Senses Grounding – I first learned this technique from a friend in 1992 when I was in my mid-twenties and struggling in all areas of my life. I still do this when I wake up in the middle of the night with my thoughts racing.

Use your five senses to reconnect you to the here and now. Silently or aloud, go through your five senses:

Five things you can see.

Five things you can hear.

Five things you can taste.

Five things you can touch.

Five things you can smell.

Bonus one that I add – five things you're currently feeling (emotionally). To me, this is the most important part of the process because it usually lets me understand what's behind my anxiety.

Take five slow, deep breaths to end the first round.

Repeat the process and do four, then keep counting down. It's often pitch black in our bedroom when I wake up and cannot see anything but darkness, I simply name what I know is there. *I see the armoire. I see our wedding portrait. There are our closet doors ...*

Please note, grounding is deeply personal. What works for one person, may not at all for another.

5. Breath Work

Even though breathing is controlled by our individual autonomic nervous systems, we do not all breathe the same. It depends on whether your home away from home is ventral, sympathetic or dorsal.

If you're a shallow breather like me, you wake up more like Tigger, high-energy in sympathetic (fight or flight). Your staccato breathing unintentionally stresses out your body worse. Practice slowing down your breathing, so you can think calmer and feel more in control.

If you tend to be more low energy, in dorsal (freeze or shutdown) like Eeyore, you should breathe differently to energize yourself and to reclaim your power.

I use the free meditation app, Oak, on my phone and

love it. Oak offers meditations (guided and unguided) for various time lengths (5 – 30 minutes), breathing exercises, ways to help you sleep, tracks your progress and more. It's easy to follow and the merit badges delight the *over*functioner in me.

I was trying so hard to find relief after the fire, but my own breathing was making that harder to do, so I began working with a breath coach in 2019 (yes, that's a thing).

Erin K. Bishop, M.A. has a Master's in Health and Wellness coaching, in addition to being a certified breath therapist and awesome person. That process has given me so many insights that my thinking brain had never imagined (like writing this book!) and facing some shame issues with a professional.

When I DO practice breathing differently, I feel more connected overall – my mind, my body and my breath are all one. Plus, I'm able to better calm myself in the heat of the moment.

That may sound woo-woo, but it works.

Erin says it best, "The most powerful tool we have is right under our very nose. Through the breath, we can change our emotional state, calm us down or energize us, whatever we need in that moment."[5]

Breathing to Calm Yourself

Oak says Box Breathing (also called four-square breathing) is a technique to heighten performance and concentration. Plus, it's a potent stress reliever used by athletes, Navy SEALS, and yoga practitioners.

Box Breathing – Inhale fully through your nose for four seconds, hold for four seconds, exhale fully through your mouth for four seconds, then hold for four seconds. That's what makes it a square: 4-4-4-4). Repeat. One recommended set is 1 minute, 4 seconds. Note: always discontinue use if feeling light-headed.

As you strengthen your breathing, you can breathe in and out for longer, but if you're trying to relax, then you want your exhalations to be twice as long as your inhalations: two breathes in/four out, four breaths in/eight out, five breaths in/ten out. Do what feels right in the moment.

For your thoughts, do whatever relaxes you: focus on counting your breaths, mentally set your worries aside by placing them one by one in the container of your choice – a trunk or a pretty box. Notice and befriend the feelings coming up, or mentally say whatever you need to hear. *It's okay, you're safe, you're just frustrated/overwhelmed, this too shall pass* …

There is no right or wrong here. Trust your instincts for what you need in the moment.

This is why I like Oak. I just follow along with the visuals for the breathing exercises. It tells me exactly when to breathe, how long to hold and so on.

Breathing to Energize Yourself

Oak calls this breath, "Awake" and says it's the perfect replacement for coffee. Use this technique either first thing in the morning, or during an afternoon energy slump for a quick burst of energy and alertness.

Awake Breath – Inhale fully through your nose for six seconds, then exhale fully through your mouth for two seconds. Repeat. One recommended set is 40 seconds. Discontinue if you feel lightheaded.

Most of all, be patient. Breathing a new way takes practice.

6. Meditation

I have a client who says meditation for her is like, "Eating glass."

I get it. I've always joked that it's hard for my *mind* and my *behind* to be in the same place at once. I've practiced mindfulness on and off for years, but Mark and I got into a regular practice soon after our house fire when he found a weekly centering prayer group at a local church. That one hour each Saturday became our saving grace. Six months later we chose meditation for our daily practice during the 40 days of Lent. We did not do it every day, but I bet we did it at least 35 days and have been hooked ever since.

Meditation, mindfulness, centering prayer – whatever you want to call it, it's crucial to practice staying "in the moment", which is extra hard because pretty much everything these days makes us want to escape. If we're not careful, one negative thought can snowball into a "parade of horribles."

My life sucks, it has always sucked, and it will suck until the day I die, broke and alone.

See what I mean?

If you struggle with meditation, or have tried it but felt like a failure, or are a newbie, please stay with me – I have a different suggestion than sitting with your body pretzeled together, while chanting *ommmmmm* (even though there's science proving the benefits of this sound).

It's Not Your Fault if You Struggle with Meditation

You already understand that this pandemic has already caused your nervous system to freak out. Slowing down might seem even scarier. If you're used to being constantly on the go, physically or emotionally, meditation can feel panicky.

Depending on your personal history, it makes sense why many don't like to be immobilized. Our nervous system resists all changes – even positive ones. It can feel traumatizing.

Benefits of Meditation

Even if your mind hates meditation, the benefits are worth the effort.

- Lowers your blood pressure.
- Lowers your heart rate.
- Slows your respiratory rate.
- Improves your blood circulation.
- Decreases perspiration.
- Decreases stress and anxiety.
- Lowers your cortisol levels.[6]

If you're new to meditation, or find the whole process torturous, try walking meditation because it's easier for starters.

Walking Meditation

You want to walk slowly, like ridiculously so, as if you're in a trance. If you worry you'll look strange, do your walking meditation in a secluded area like your backyard or uncrowded spot out in nature. Or, stay inside.

If possible, put your phone away, so you won't be tempted to stroll and scroll. You can either set the timer nearby or just do a certain number of laps.

Your pace should be s-l-o-w and steady. The purpose is to not arrive anywhere, but to unwind your mind. To just be.

Focus on whatever speaks to you. Watch your feet as you walk – heel, foot, toe. Slow your breath. Try to pay attention to each step.

As you walk, notice how your body feels. If you want, observe the world around you, as if you're watching a movie.

Pay attention to your thoughts because your mind *will* wander.

That's okay. This is actually part of your practice. Don't berate yourself for "not doing it right." Simply begin again.

If you want, pause when your mind wanders because it will. What is distracting you? Then return your attention to the rise and fall of each step. Since it's easier to walk mindfully than to do a seated meditation, try to go for at least fifteen minutes. If that's too much, do whatever you cane. Some is better than none.

There is no right or wrong way to walk mindfully, you just want to slow down your mind, and therefore your body. To quiet that chatter in your brain. To inch yourself up the elevator of your nervous system to a more ventral state.

To just be.

More Traditional Meditation

Sit however is most comfortable. It does not matter whether it's a chair, on your bed, on the floor with your legs cross or stretched out. The most important aspect is that your back and feet feel supported. If it physically hurts you, then it's extra hard to relax and find a flow state.

Lying down would not be my first choice because it's too easy to fall asleep, but if that's your preference, then go for it.

Do not expect yourself to be free from thoughts. You simply want to turn down the volume from the chatter in your brain. Monkey mind is real.

Start small, like five minutes. I believe this is the biggest mistake that beginners make. They set out to do a 20-to-30-minute meditation, then mentally crash and burn. Feeling like failures.

Baby steps.

Meditation Apps

Again, I love Oak, but I've also heard good things about Calm, Headspace, 10% Happier (which is said to be made for fidgety skeptics).

Don't be afraid to use nothing at all. Complete silence is also great, too. Many people's lives are full of too much mental noise.

Different Types of Meditation

If you decide to Do It Yourself, here are some suggestions. Try whichever you feel you need, try one for several days in a row, then switch.

Focused attention – This is a great place to start because it's so simple. Pick something to focus on, then stare at it. I like to light a candle and watch the flame, which is odd since I'm the fire gal, but go figure. Others find the flame distracting and focus on an unmoving object.

Count your breaths – Follow the steps in #5 Breath Work.

Mantra – Find a word or short phrase to focus on as you inhale and exhale. Breathe in "love," breathe out "stress". Or, breathe in "thank you," breathe out "thank you." Just choose words that are not too emotionally charged for you.

Chanting *om* – Scientists found in a 2018 study that chanting the ancient
mantra of *om* is associated with an experience of relaxation in the autonomic nervous system, and deactivation of limbic brain regions, which controls emotions, memories and arousal.[7] Some people pronounce *om* with a long "o" sound, followed by a vibrating "m." Others prefer to separate the sounds, so it more of an "ah-oo-mm." I do both, and go with whatever I'm feeling in the moment.

Body scan – Start at your head, then mentally pass through your body and bring attention to what hurts, aches, feels tense, or any other sensations or insights.

Visualization – This one is great because it's focusing on your future self, or something you want to manifest. Instead of concentrating on your breath, picture what you want to create in your life: more money, a thinner you, a new car.

Everything is Meditation

That may be the most Zen thing I've ever said. Meditation is just another opportunity for practice. Practice being more mindful. You don't need a special setup or anything. Be mindful while you wash the dishes, make your bed, do chores around the house, while sitting at your desk.

This may seem hard at first. Slowing down your thoughts will slow down your breath, your heart rate and help you move up your nervous system elevator.

Stressed out does not have to be your normal.

You deserve more.

A Few Pointers

- **Start small** – Begin with five minutes, then work your way up to 20 or 30 minutes.
- **Don't get caught in the "how"** – This website says to meditate first thing in the morning, while that article says to count my breaths, but a friend told me you've got to sit up straight. Forget all that. Do what works best for you.
- **Expect your mind to wander** – The goal is not to clear your mind of thoughts, but rather to turn down the volume of the mental chatter in your brain.
- **Compassion and curiosity** – Changing patterns is hard, sacred work. That happens faster when you're kinder to yourself, rather than berating yourself for one more thing you're doing wrong.
- **Befriend your emotions** – By now you should understand there are no good or bad feelings. All emotions are equally important because they're all carrying messages about your unique stress patterns.
- **You can meditate anywhere** – At home, in your car, waiting in line. I've even walked into a public restroom stall to quiet my mind before an important meeting.
- **Do it whenever you can** – Sure, it's great if you meditate around the same time because that trains your nervous system. *Oh yeah, it's time to meditate and calm down.* However, some is better than none.
- **High–five yourself afterwards** – Because each time you meditate, you're rewiring your brain a little more.

My Best Meditation Advice I Do Not Always Follow

Whenever I feel too busy to meditate, that is absolutely, positively when it's essential for me to sit my arse down and to slow my roll. When I do, I'm so much more capable to handle the challenges that life throws my way.

When I do not – let's just say, I pay. It actually takes less time to meditate than for me to go back later and undo the emotional damage I inflict on myself and others when I'm in screaming sympathetic.

Meditation also helps me feel more connected to God, but it works whether you're a believer or not. Just feeling more connected to nature, to others, to yourself – those are all reasons to at least try meditation.

7. The Critical Voice in Your Head

If you want more health, happiness and success, if you want to experience deeper, richer connections with yourself and others, then you must learn to be kinder to yourself.

Most of us would never talk to others the way our internal dialogue goes, so try talking more to yourself like you would a friend. Or, think back to the beginning – *who is your why*?

If they were struggling with this same issue, would you berate them like you do yourself?

Probably not.

The quicker you learn to be kinder to yourself more consistently, the quicker your life will improve. This can be a challenge, so ...

8. Have More Fun

Since our nervous system is hardwired to look for danger, our cavemen brains tend to see the negative instead of the positive in life. Be more intentional to seek joy, to laugh, be inspired or to have more fun.

That can be challenging during a global pandemic, but it's not only possible, it's necessary. As we inch our way to a new normal, we need to be our best selves to pick up the pieces and help those who are struggling, which is everyone. We all need each other.

This isn't selfish. It's important self-care. Remember, we need to all bring our A-games in the future, so you need to be at your best.

Watch Funny or Inspiring Videos Online – I like to find 3 – 10 minute clips online of my favorite comedians to make me laugh. There are also endless YouTubers out there who are making the most of dark times. Another favorite is keynote speakers at college graduations. That's when people are doling out their best advice. All of the above helps boost my spirits when I have insomnia or need a daytime pick me up.

Watch Lighthearted TV Shows or Movies – I'm a huge "Game of Thrones" fan, but dude! Forget, *Winter is coming*. It's here. I need fun easy-breezy shows or movies to keep me positive right now.

Read a novel – Fiction is a great form of escapism since most of us are not traveling as much these days. Nonfiction is wonderful, too. Learn new topics and feed your mind. Foggy brain is real, so listen to an audiobook instead. Reading opens your mind, expands your heart and your horizons.

Get Creative – Color (adult color books are the best!), draw, paint, write, dance.

Game Night – Play cards or board games to laugh and have a good time.

Keep a Gratitude Journal – This is when I use a pretty little journal. I picked this practice back up several months into the pandemic. At the end of the day, I sit on the edge of my bed (which is better than the edge of a mental cliff) and write 3 things I'm grateful for from that day. It makes me pay more attention to my life, and seek out moments that are more joyful, happy, funny, endearing. In neuroscience terms, it makes me wear more ventral sunglasses as I experience my everyday world. Plus, it's such a nicer way to go to sleep. Another great way to seek out joy ...

9. Keep Connecting with Others

Do not isolate.

Hello? Global pandemic?

That's challenging since we were grounded and sent home to COVID jail in the beginning, but you need to stay connected to people. We're biologically hardwired for community, so your subconscious mind is missing your tribe.

Phone calls, texts, emails, online through FaceTime or Zoom, or if it's allowed in your area, socially-distanced in person while wearing masks.

There are online groups for pretty much anything: knitting, Harry Potter fans, people who love to fly drones, pugs, essential oils, stamp collecting, or kick-boxing. You name it.

Currently, Zoom offers free accounts for 40-minute sessions, with your video camera on or off (whatever your technology allows and whatever you prefer).

Connect with others.

10. Keep Investing in Yourself

Whatever your Top 3 Struggles are – you are not alone. There are endless online resources: articles, posts, videos, books, groups. Buy books locally, or online, check out information from your library. We've never had more ways to expand our horizons.

Utilize them.

There are so many healing modalities. I could list literally 100 different activities, but here are a few that I've either tried, or personally know someone who has had success with it. Some are more woo-woo than others, but if they help you feel better, that's great!

Still, try them at your own risk.

Acupuncture – I thought it would freak me out to feel like a poked pin cushion, but I loved it. This was one of the first things that helped me after our fire.

Biofeedback – Mindy-body technique that involves visual or auditory feedback to gain control over your nervous system. I know many believers.

Breath work – This is the fastest way for me to improve my mood.

EFT (Emotional Freedom Technique) – Better known as Tapping, where you "tap" on the pressure points in your body to release stress or anxiety. Many find it incredibly helpful. It's easy, and you can do it on your own.

EMDR (Eye Movement Desensitization Reprocessing) – It's designed to alleviate the distress associated with traumatic memories. I've never tried EMDR, but have friends who claim it was life-changing in dealing with deep wounds.

Exercise – Running, lifting weights, dancing, hiking, walking, sports, whatever body movement you enjoy.

Floating – Immersing yourself in a salinated body of water for a sensory deprivation experience. It's very relaxing.

HRV (Heart-rate variability training) – My husband digs this. It's great for folks not interested in coaching or therapy.

Meditation (or centering prayer) – Discussed earlier in this chapter. It was truly one of our saving graces after the fire.

Neurofeedback – A type of biofeedback where an EEG machine measures your brainwaves and hack your nervous system neurologically. Think of your mind as an old-timey TV where the picture is scrambled and out of focus. Neurofeedback helps clear away the static to give your mind and body a clearer picture. People have found it either mind-blowing, or *meh*.

Reiki – Hands-on healing through transferring energy. I've never done it, but know folks really into this.

Therapy – My dad thought therapy was for weak people.

He was wrong. It's the bravest thing in the world to sit down in front of a stranger and say, "What I'm doing is not working. Help me find a better way."

Yoga – I "heart" all yoga: power, restorative, aerial, Kundalini, Ashtanga, slow-flow, the variations are endless. So are the benefits.

11. Find a Qualified Professional

This probably should be number one, but I wanted to offer you several free or inexpensive options first. Whatever the next step is on your healing journey, keep searching until you find the right support. Whether it's a medical doctor for a physical issue, a nutritionist, or a practitioner to help with your emotional health.

Google is your friend. With whatever you're seeking in terms of emotional support – *life coach, therapist, psychologist* – consider including words like *nervous system*, *polyvagal, trauma-informed, trauma trained or somatic*.

You want someone who not only can help you identify your stress patterns, but who can also guide you from moving those fight-flight-or-freeze stress blocks *stuck inside your body*. Time, patience and practice are key.

At first, it's almost impossible to recognize your own stress patterns because they are your emotional blind spots. You want someone who is encouraging and won't shame you since your patterns all make perfect sense in the larger context of your life.

All you have to do is the next right action on your healing journey.

12. Baby Steps

Please do not try to overhaul everything about your life overnight. All, go big or go home!

No. That is setting yourself up for failure.

All you have to do it take one baby step today.

One, ugly, imperfect baby step.

Then, one more tomorrow.

And, so on.

You can do it.

Speaking of ...

Do This!

Create your own Stress Less Action Plan so that you have your next steps.

1. Self-care Toolbox

Solo activities (self-regulation):

_____

_____

_____

Connecting with others (co-regulation):

_____

_____

_____

2. Daily self-care

(Remember to focus on what you can control – what you eat, drink, sleep, moving your body, activities from your self-care toolbox to help keep you regulated):

_____

_____

_____

3. What are your next steps to improve your physical ailments?

_____

_____

_____

_____

4. What are your next steps to improve your Top 3 Struggles?

_____

_____

_____

_____

5. What is your Home Away from Home emotional state of your nervous system (ventral – sympathetic – dorsal)? What is the #1 way it is showing up for you these days?

_____

_____

_____

_____

Attachment Styles: Secure Anxious Avoidant Disorganized

6. What's one baby step you can make regularly to move to a more secure attachment?

_____

_____

_____

_____

Remember, WHO IS YOUR WHY? Keep thinking of him, her, them + you as you continue to transform your stress.

Notes

1. Stevenson, S. (2016). Sleep smarter 21 essential strategies to sleep your way to a better body, better health, and bigger success. Rodale.
2. Associated Press. (2020, March 31). Booze buying surges;

senators push airlines for cash refunds. AP NEWS. https://apnews.com/article/ c407ecb931c6c528b4cceb0ecc216f0c.

3. Stevenson, S. (2016). Sleep smarter 21 essential strategies to sleep your way to a better body, better health, and bigger success. Rodale.

4. Chevalier, G., Patel, S., Weiss, L., Chopra, D., & Mills, P. J. (2018). *The Effects of Grounding (Earthing) on Bodyworkers' Pain and Overall Quality of Life: A Randomized Controlled Trial*. PubMed.gov. https://pubmed.ncbi.nlm.nih.gov/30448083/.

5. Bishop, E. K. (2020, September 17). personal communication.

6. Mayo Clinic Staff. (2020, April 22). Meditation: A simple, fast way to reduce stress. Mayo Clinic. https://www.mayoclinic.org/tests-procedures/meditation/in-depth/meditation/art-20045858.

7. Rao, N. P., Deshpande, G., Gangadhar, K. B., Arasappa, R., Varambally, S., Venkatasubramanian, G., & Ganagadhar, B. N. (2018, August 3). *Directional brain networks underlying OM chanting*. Asian Journal of Psychiatry. https://www.sciencedirect.com/science/article/pii/ S1876201818302004.

Conclusion

Rising from the Ashes

Although I thought the fire was one of the worst things to ever happen to me, it turned out to be one of the best things ever.

It forced me to deal with so many issues – topics I didn't even realize were problems until my life got so much better.

And, it's so much better!

The fire alarm continues to ring through my brain and body at times. It doesn't happen nearly as often and the volume is much lower, but it still happens.

That doesn't frighten me like it did because now I understand my stress patterns and realize I'm just being triggered again. It has sounded off inside me for a reason, so I clear away the smoke to find the real problem and the noise goes away.

Good Luck

Thank you for reading my book. You've given me purpose during one of the most bizarre times in modern history. The #1 thing I want to leave you with from reading this is ...

Hope.

No matter what has happened to you in the past. No matter what your personal house fire is, no matter how awful, unfair or bad it was – you can move beyond your pain to enjoy deeper, richer connections to yourself and others.

I believe this with all my heart.

I've also experienced this myself, in my marriage, with my kids, friends, family and have been honored to walk my clients through similar transformations.

The more we change our inner world, the more it changes our outer world. That's huge because humanity desperately needs us listening to each other, talking *to* each other, instead of screaming *at* each other.

Within ourselves as individuals.

As families.

As organizations.

As countries.

The world needs healing because life shouldn't feel like a house fire.

I wish you well.

Will You Do a Gal a Favor?

Thank you for reading *Transforming Your Stress*. Will you please leave an honest review online for my book at the sales site of your choice? It would mean so much to me because that encourages other readers to discover my work.

I appreciate you so much.

Let's Stay in Touch

Please join my email list at marcymckay.com if you'd like to stay connected.

Follow me on Instagram: @marcymmmckay

Facebook: authormarcymckay

Courses to Help You

 **Book Accelerator Video Course**

Follow alongside Marcy's book to learn how to thrive more & stress less.

https://marcymckay.teachable.com/p/transform-your-stress

*23 videos (over 3.5 hours total) introducing each chapter + interviews with fellow coaches to inspire you.

*Downloadable workbook, with 20+ exercises, worksheets & assessments.

*Pinpoint your stress origins, as well as your physical/emotional/behavioral stress symptoms.

*One-year access to the course.

https://marcymckay.teachable.com/p/transform-your-stress

Hope and Relief are on the Way

ReDesign Your Life is a deep dive, DIY online course for those who really want someone to take them by the hand and guide them to change.

https://marcymckay.teachable.com/p/redesign-your-life

*6 Weeks with Marcy: 10+ hours worth of videos to educate you on how stress shows up in your life, so you know how to change.

*Downloadable Workbooks: for each session, with exercises & assessments to guide your transformation.

*Videos from Actual Group Coaching Sessions: providing you with multiple perspectives.

*One-year's access to the program + everything is downloadable: 12-month access, with all the videos, Powerpoint presentations and workbooks are downloadable to keep.

https://marcymckay.teachable.com/p/redesign-your-life

Chapter Takeaways

My Book Accelerator course, *Transform Your Stress*, is available online to enhance your learning. It has all the book's exercises and assessments in one downloadable workbook, as well as 3.5 hours worth of bonus video content:

https://marcymckay.teachable.com/p/transform-your-stress/

INTRODUCTION

Your stress symptoms are not just connected to the pandemic, but they are also related to the past. *Your* past.

PART 1: YOUR STRESS

Chapter 1 – Your Stress is 100% Real: Even if you and your family are safe and healthy since March 2020, your stress is not imagined. It is very real and serves an important biological function in your life.

Chapter 2 – It's ~~Not that Bad~~: There is a wide range of feelings associated with our 24/7 lifestyle, and it takes a great deal of energy for you to hold space for so many competing emotions.

Chapter 3 – Let's Rip Off the Band-aid: Your old life is gone forever and should be mourned. Identify *who* is the person(s) for whom you want to change so that you enjoy more health and happiness.

PART 2: YOUR STRESS PATTERNS

Chapter 4 – Your Stress Origins: Tracing the origins of your stress patterns whether they began in childhood or as an adult often provide "ah-ha!" moments. These origins might be personal, private, and painful, but it's not the blame game to your parents or whoever raised you.

Chapter 5 – Do Not Get Hung Up on Words: Trauma is misunderstood and much more than a one-time event: war, a car wreck, physical or sexual abuse. Everyone has experienced varying degrees of trauma and those past stressors are impacting you today.

Chapter 6 – Let's Get Physical: Trauma changes you from the inside out. Pinpointing your physical ailments assists in tracking your stress patterns.

Chapter 7 – Emotions in Motion: Our physical body can be changed by the emotions we experience. Provides a list of common physical complaints, linked to their possible emotional connections.

Chapter 8 – Your Stress Busters Toolbox: It's important to create your own toolbox of support during these uncertain times, activities that you do on your own, and with others for connection. Try the Brain Savvy app for more self-awareness and a higher mindset.

PART 3: THE SCIENCE BEHIND YOUR STRESS

Chapter 9 – Because ... Science: Your nervous system

controls the majority of your bodily functions, in addition to your feelings. Your nervous system has three, predictable emotional states: ventral (connection), sympathetic (fight or flight) and dorsal (freeze or shutdown). Regulating your nervous system is the key to changing your stress patterns and why you've felt stuck or unable to change in the past.

Chapter 10 – Nervous System 101: Your nervous system cannot skip ahead between your three emotional states. You cannot avoid being triggered. Stop resisting your feelings, positive or negative, because they all serve as important messengers for you.

Chapter 11 – Your Home Away from Home: We each have a home away from home, our nervous system's preferred emotional state when we feel stressed. Safety is the key to change, but setbacks and mistakes are actually part of the process, too.

Chapter 12 – Attachment is Everything: The psychological science behind attachment styles explains yourself and others: how valuable you feel, how much you trust others, how effectively you interact with others, how social you are, and how you handle conflict. The four attachment styles are secure, anxious, avoidant and disorganized. These attachment styles explain our relationship to people, place, money, work and more.

PART 4: YOUR STRESS BLUEPRINT

Chapter 13 – Your Top 3 Struggles: Your body is responding perfectly according to your unique stress patterns. Identify your Top 3 Struggles in managing your anxiety.

Chapter 14 – Your Snapshot Moment(s): Your Top 3

Struggles are often closely related to your snapshot moment, which is your root cause and came from your stress origins. This is where your coping strategies began.

Chapter 15 – Critical Voices: There is at least one negative voice subconsciously playing inside your head that is typically connected to your Top 3 Struggles. These are the thoughts beneath your thoughts that you might not even realize are there.

Chapter 16 – Stressed Out: *Over*-and-*under*functioning are patterned responses to anxiety, which often stem from childhood, but can be changed.

Chapter 17 – Connecting the Dots: Finding the link between your Top 3 Struggles, your snapshot moment(s), your Critical Voice, and your attachment style could be the key to understanding your stress patterns.

Chapter 18 – Putting out the Fire: The variety of ways to heal your stress patterns: sleep, your gut health, the foods you eat, alcohol consumption, limiting your screen time, journaling, exercise, Vitamin D through sunshine, grounding, breath work, meditation, the importance of connection, education, finding a qualified professional to work with. Includes your overall Stress Less Action Plan to create concrete changes in your life. Your biggest superpower to transform is the ability to reconnect with yourself and others after setbacks, mistakes, misunderstandings or whatever challenges life throws your way.

Resource Guide

Bessel van der Kolk, MD – besselvanderkolk.com

Brené Brown, PhD, LMSW – brenebrown.com

Deb Dana, LMSW – rhythmofregulation.com

Diane Poole Heller, PhD – dianepooleheller.com

Erin K. Bishop, MA – abreathofwellness.com

Justin Sunseri, LMFT – justinlmft.com

Kelly Turner, PhD – kelly-turner.com

Laurel Mellin, PhD – ebtconnect.net

Louise Hay – louisehay.com

Mastin Kipp – mastinkipp.com

Melissa Hallmark Kerr, PhD – brainsavvytraining.com

Nicole LePera, PhD – theholisticpsychologist.com

Peter Levine, PhD – somaticexperiencing.com

Stephen Porges, PhD – stephenporges.com

Shawn Stevenson – themodelhealthshow.com

Meditation Apps

Oak Meditation – oakmeditation.com

Headspace – headspace.com

10% Happier – tenpercent.com

Mindset App

Brain Savvy – brainsavvytraining.com

Acknowledgments

It's impossible to thank all the appropriate people after your family faces a house fire. The love, the prayers, people near and far who lifted us has been beyond humbling. We had the best neighbors for 17 years: the Austins, the Novaks, the DuPriests, the Baays, the Millers, Dr. Curtis, the Parkeys, the Rusks and the Steeds. We miss you, but appreciate that you still invite us to block parties!

To everyone in Sunday Canyon, thank you for welcoming us with open arms in our new community.

The good folks at St. Andrew's Episcopal Church, thank you for loving us through such a difficult time. I appreciate you living daily the message of Presiding Bishop Michael Curry, *If it's not about love, it's not about God.*

Special thanks to Reverend Mark Weathers who was then the pastor at First Christian Church – your weekly hour of silence during Centering Prayer each Saturday began the slow process of transformation for my Mark and me. We're forever grateful. Add everyone from Palace Coffee (Krystal and Patrick Burns) + Barrel & Pie (Kevin Friemel and Marcus Snead) ... healing through caffeine and pizza was the perfect RX for us!

To my writing buddies, Jennifer Archer and A.G. Howard. Our critique group may not be together anymore, but you two cheering me on virtually made such a difference. I love you both, and your friendship means the world to me.

Erin Perrigo, Michelle Hydeck, Kristen Freyja Solberg, Jen Gima – my new coaching buddies. Y'all have walked this path with me since Day One of our ProsperX program.

Many thanks for all the encouragement via emails, DMs and giggles (both in person and online).

To my mentor and coach, Mastin Kipp. There are no words to describe the impact you've made in my life. You, Jenna Hall, Kate Hannon, Dylan Schmidt and everyone else at VIP showed me how to turn my pain into purpose. Thank you!

To Eric Hutchins and Pamela Fagan Hutchins at SkipJack Publishing, I appreciate you giving my books a home, both fiction and non-fiction. I'm honored to associate with talented authors like Pamela, Ken Oder, R.L. Nolen and Gay Yellen.

To Bobbye Marrs – you, above all others, are the guardian angel of this book. You brought order to chaos, calm to my fears, and shepherded my manuscript when I worried all was lost. Your knowledge, patience, and gifts know no bounds and I'm forever grateful for you. I look forward to seeing how your voice heals this world ... because it will!

To Erin Bishop – you taught me how to breathe life into this dream. Thank you for walking me through my fears, so I could be of service to others.

To my family – Mom, Greg and Molly. Families speak without words, and I feel your love wherever I go. Thank you for your excitement about this book and for showing others how families *can* heal together. We've been through so much; I think Daddy would be proud of us all.

To my father-in-law, Dick McKay, the nine months you let us stay at the cabin saved Mark and me. Truly. To have such a happy place during such an unhappy time was nothing short of life-saving. Many thanks.

Mark, Mason and Luke. You three are my everything, and I love you with all my heart. You're the main reason I choose do the painful, but powerful work to transform myself so our family can be happier and healthier. There's also no one else I'd rather play Exploding Kittens with, especially on the rare occasions that I win.

To my readers – stories matter. Kindness matters. Now more than ever before, we need to connect with each other to create a better tomorrow for *all*. Thank you for taking in my words and hopefully letting them impact your life the way they have mine. I appreciate you giving me the gift of your time.

M3

Book Club Discussion Questions

1. What is your biggest takeaway after reading *Transforming Your Stress*?

2. Fun and play are important parts of healing trauma. What can you do to incorporate more fun or joy into your life these days? What are a few new activities you would like to try in the future?

3. Most people have not experienced an actual fire, but many have in the metaphorical sense (death, divorce or some other heartbreak). What has this book shown you about your own personal house fire(s)?

4. In learning about attachment styles (secure, anxious, avoidant and disorganized), what insights does this give you to someone you struggle to understand "why" they are the way they are?

5. In discussing attachment styles, Marcy McKay lists eight areas in our lives: romance, family, friends, spirituality/religion, career/business, finances, health/fitness, fun/recreation/play. Which one do you feel like needs more balance? What's one thing you can do to start making changes there?

6. Who are the *over/under*functioners in your inner circle? How do you need to personally evolve in this regard?

7. Marcy offers several suggestions to help "put out the fire" of your stress: sleep, gut health, diet, limiting your screen time, journaling, exercise, getting more sunshine,

grounding, breath work, meditation, having more fun, connecting with others, finding a qualified professional. Which of these intrigued you, and why? Which are you skeptical about, and why?

8. It's easy to focus on what all you're doing "wrong." Can you name two or three things that you're doing well in dealing with your anxieties, even if it's just a little bit?

9. Sometimes, our stress origin(s) can feel like a curse. What are some "unexpected blessings" in yours? For example, a chaotic childhood might mean you adapt well to change. If you endured severe trauma, you probably have great inner strength.

10. What's one tiny change you can make in your life now to create healthier stress patterns? Don't think BIG. That's overwhelming. Think small steps.

About the Author

Since 1996, Marcy McKay has worked with nonprofit boards, businesses and individuals on how to work and play better together in the sandbox of life. She's also the award-winning author of the debut novel, *Pennies from Burger Heaven*, which tells the story about a homeless girl who wakes up at the cemetery to discover her mama is missing, changing her life forever (300+Amazon reviews).

In 2017, Marcy's own world turned upside down after her family's house fire. That crisis sent her on a journey to Humpty Dumpty herself back together again. The experience was so incredible that Marcy wrote *Transforming Your Stress* to help others. She is a corporate speaker and facilitates workshops on stress management, how to find your purpose and live your best life, as well as other inspiring topics.

Connect with Marcy:

Website: marcymckay.com

Email: marcy@marcymckay.com

Instagram: @authormarcymckay

Facebook: authormarcymckay

Excerpt - Marcy McKay's Novel

When Marcy is not coaching clients, leading workshops, or spinning plates, she also writes fast-paced fiction.

Check out her angsty protagonist, Copper Daniels, who's known more trauma in her young life than most, but always manages to be the hero in her own story.

Pennies from Burger Heaven was a 2016 Shelf Unbound Winner, and has 300+ Amazon reviews. Readers who enjoy *Where the Crawdads Sing* will love this book. This story came to Marcy in 2018 while visiting her father's cemetery ...

Me and Mama live here at the cemetery, by the Warrior Angel statue. It's our home. He always stands high on those four pedestals, with his dark wings stretched wide. That stone sword stays in his left hand, while he keeps his right out toward Burger Heaven. Asking God for help.

Who knew angels were beggars like me?

"Feeling better, Mama?" I say, then see her empty sleeping bag.

The dark green just stares back.

"Mama?" I yawn and look around to nothing but quiet graves.

She's probably gone to the bathroom. I start to lie back down 'til last night socks me in the gut. All her tears, all her crazy talk, how she got so sick. I eyeball the statue, but if he knows where she is, he's not saying.

I better go find her myself. She needed me then and she'll need me now. Especially if she's still pukey.

Climbing out of my sleeping bag, my legs feel stiff from their frosty sleep. I keep my bright blue coat zipped with the hoodie up, then rub my gloves together to get warm. My breath snakes out and my toes poke all wiggly-like through the holes in my sneakers. I can't walk in a straight line here like I do down most streets. I zigzag through all the headstones, bushes and trees. Patches of snow from last week's storm surround graves tucked into pockets of shade. Dew sparkles like diamonds on grass that's actually green on this side of the cemetery.

Everything shines brighter for the Somebodies of the world.

As I pass a turned-over vase of red roses, I set it upright. The droopy petals still smell flowery. I call out to Mama.

The birds chirp at me overhead.

Her screams from last night clatter through me again. She dropped to her knees and sobbed against my legs, *"I've got to chaaaaaaaaaaaaange."*

I move a little faster. You can't miss Mama. She's supermodel thin and tall, with leafy-green eyes and tiny flecks of gold in 'em. Maybe she's not like a real supermodel, but she's definitely taller than me and every bit as bone skinny. She wears her jet-black hair straight down and parted in the middle. She thinks she looks like Cher. I saw the singer once on TV and didn't think so, but wasn't dumb enough to say it out loud, thank you very little. Mama doesn't have movie-star teeth, either, though she does wear a silver jacket made of real rabbit fur like they do in Hollywood. Well, it's more dingy than silver now, but I still want one just like it when I grow up.

If it was summertime, you'd see Mama's blue angel wings tattooed across her shoulders and back. She did that after I was born, inked in to protect us both. It fits her, too. She always looks ready to fly away.

The breeze swishes through the trees as I call out for her again.

Mama better get home soon 'cause O'Dell will show up for work any second, then there'll be hell to pay. We may live in the Historic Section of the cemetery, but they won't let us spend eternity here when we keel over. There'll be no flashy statues or real flowers. We'll be buried back in the Nobody Section. That used to be the only spot they allowed the Blacks, the Mexicans, the Chinamen and other No Names, too.

I pass David Marshall's grave where we took care of our morning business yesterday. His headstone is shaped like an actual tree stump. Broken trunks are supposed to be a sign for death, a life cut short, like his buried body isn't clue enough.

My gut twists. Maybe she went to the pond to feed the ducks, even though we always do that together. I'll check, but first I squat behind this elm tree. We try to switch bathrooms each time to be nice. They may be stiffers, but who wants to get peed on every day?

After I'm done, I follow a well-worn path. The big cloud above looks like someone is laughing with their mouth open wide. I can do that. I make Mama giggle so hard water squirts straight from her nose. It's funny-gross and gross-funny. You know something's hilarious when you make 'em rock snot.

We're way more than mother and daughter. We're business partners and best friends. Mama says there are over fifty thousand bodies here at Eternal Peace. When I was little she said that meant there were over fifty thousand stories, each filled with glad, mad and sad. People who made it well past their hundredth birthdays. Husbands who leave gifts on their wives' graves, while their girlfriends wait in the car. The worst are parents visiting their little ones at Baby Land. You can hear 'em crying in the wind at night. Their sadness makes you want to disapp—

That thought stops me. My world turns topsy-turvy and I have to steady myself against a grave. Scared torches my belly. Why didn't I think of it before?

The *Disappeareds*.

Rumor has it that there's a Street Killer on the loose in Paradise, murdering the Nobodies of the world. Folks will be there one second, then poof! They're gone.

Disappeared.

But, that's happening miles away from Eternal Peace. We're safe here.

Right?

"Mama!" I screech.

Ripping my lucky penny from my pocket, I pull my gloves off to rub Mr. Lincoln's beard extra hard, commanding him to find her quick. I rush through the graves. Next, we stopped at Ronald Freedmont's. My gaze darts around for her. The black iron fence loops all the way around the grounds like little, pointy soldiers. "Eternal Peace" is written in gold across the twin gates that stay locked after dark to keep the goodness in and the badness out.

What if it stopped working last night?

Biting my lip, I race faster. Salty tears try to climb up my throat, but I shove 'em down. They do me no good and I need to stay focused. Plus, Mama hates wusses. She wasn't at the pond and she's not at Ronald Freedmont's now. I lean against his too-tall grave and try to ignore the headache knocking at my brain. Mama says Ronnie here must've thought a lot of himself 'cause his name's plastered across the marble in huge, scrawly letters. A mint bush sprouts beside him. We come here every day to eat the leaves to clean our teeth. His plant grows and grows, like he waters himself with regret. That sounds like something stuck in your teeth, but it means sad, wishing you'd done different. I know all about that.

Last night, most of all. My mind whirls. Maybe she's lost, or kidnapped, or dea—

No. The Street Killer didn't get her. She's not a *Disappeared*. She's too smart for that. I'll find her any minute.

I cram the mint in my mouth, then head on, hollering her name 'til my throat croaks. The sun has started rising, a small orange flame against the sleepy blue sky. It looks more perfect than a picture. Today acts like another normal day. I sure hope so, but sprint harder, just in case.

Something jumps in front of me. I scream and stumble back, but catch myself in time. A jackrabbit hops by, springing through tiny spaces between the graves. I double over to rest and calm myself down. We've got our habits. We've got our routines. O'Dell and the other lazies are about to show up to not work all day. We're usually long gone by now and we always leave together.

What if she left without me?

Each step seems to chant *Ma-ma, Ma-ma, Ma-ma.* I should've waited to fall asleep after her. I should've checked on her throughout the night. I should've never slept at all.

What'd she say through all her screaming and crying?

Oh yeah, she was bad-mouthing someone. *"Asshole, thinks he can trick me ... but ... I'll show him."*

Who'd she mean? How'd he trick her? Did *showing him* get her into trouble? I trot up to a ginormous stone building. It's the Main Mausoleum at Eternal Peace and the biggest place on the grounds.

It looks like a fancy church, but a mausoleum is a cemetery house to bury Somebodies. Folks who want to stay stuck-up, even in the afterlife. We sneak inside sometimes to sleep when it's extra cold outside. I wanted to come here last night, but thought Mama was in no shape to move.

Guess I was wrong. She moved herself, all right. But where?

Creeping behind the bushes, I reach up to the window.

Locked. It won't budge. I can't believe O'Dell did his job for a change.

Yanking back my hoodie, my crazy curls spring out every which way as I zoom on from the Historic Section. I could punch O'Dell. He's such a Butt Munch. He really wants us gone. The wind moans, like it's aching for me.

The Nobody Section almost looks like nothing's back here 'til you're almost on top of it. Brown grass, tons of weeds, and most graves are just foot markers—bricks buried straight in the ground. O'Dell and his bunch never work on this side of the cemetery. Folks used to call this the Colored Section.

Mama said years ago there was this big sickness called the influenza. It was a flu that killed folks faster than the groundskeepers could dig, so they started dumping the bodies together into huge piles like trash. If the workmen then were half as worthless as O'Dell, that's not too much of a shocker.

This is our doorway in-and-out to the rest of the world. I can see from far away Mama wasn't here, but can't stop myself from checking since we passed by together last night. I walk over to my very favorite grave in all of Eternal Peace. This brick buried here on the end:

UNKNOWN NEGRO

Did they really not know his name, or did they just not care?

Anyway, he's king of the Nobodies. He's one of us.

"Where is she?" I ask him.

He's as silent as the Warrior Angel.

Maybe she's already home. Maybe we just made opposite loops and missed each other. Maybe she's there right now.

Hope fuels me as I take a different route back to check new places. Mama smells like cinnamon gum, cigarettes and sweet sweat from working so hard for us. Catch a whiff of her and you'll know a true-blue, deep-in-my-heart, looney-tunes kind of love.

All I want to do is breathe her in now and feel her hands smooth out the kinks in my hair again, while she tells me about California. We're moving there soon to start a new life. LA has palm trees and the sun shines every day of the year. We'll never be cold again.

Ever.

An invisible fist rams my gut each time she doesn't answer my calls.

Back in the Historic Section, I stop near the chapel to catch my breath. The red-bricked building has a black cross on top. They hold smaller funerals there, or when folks don't have their own church home. Naked rose bushes surround it; those thorns look ready to tear me apart. It's the one place I've never been here at the cemetery and don't want to go, but since I've had zero luck everywhere else I should check.

As I tiptoe to the porch, my hands shake like I need a fix, though I'd never do drugs 'cause it eats you from the inside out. Even worse, it gobbles up the people around you, too. I'm sweating all over, even though I see the groundskeepers and funeral people go in and out of here all the time.

I pause outside the door. Mama will spank me for sure about this, but I tug on the wooden handles anyway.

Locked.

I'm equal sad and glad 'cause I didn't want to go in there, but Mama's still missing. I should've known she wouldn't be in the chapel and race away.

I know I'm closer to home when I catch a whiff of her hurl from last night near the Vanderhausen Mausoleum. The Main Mausoleum wasn't good enough for 'em, so they built their own cemetery house. They're the snobbiest snobs. My eyes burn from the stench. I cover my mouth and keep going, wishing the wind would change direction.

The Warrior Angel stands stone still as usual. Our sleeping bags haven't budged a bit. My heart feels lost in my own body, like it doesn't know what to do without Mama. I flop in front of the statue and bury my face in my gloves. This can't be happening.

But, it is.

I make myself take three extra-slow breaths. All the folks who've gone missing were in Paradise, and that's over an hour's walk away. Besides, I still don't know for sure who's missing. That one lady was gone a while, but showed up after a bender. Everyone else are just rumors.

So far.

I sure don't want to break the rules and go out alone, but Mama sort of gave me no choice. We went straight to the Burger Heaven from here yesterday, so I guess I'll try there first. As long as I don't have to go to Paradise. It's hell on a good day, but there's no good days.

I don't have a stone sword like the Warrior Angel and I sure don't need God, but Mr. Lincoln's mojo better come back fast. I roll up our sleeping bags, then tuck 'em back in their spots—inside the lilac bush beside Miz Elsie. Her grave is shaped like two praying hands. I grab the cardboard sign Mama keeps remaking for us:

NEED MONEY FOR FOOD

GOD BLESS

She adds that last part out loud as people pass by 'cause

that pulls at their heart strings, then that pulls at their purse strings. You've got to do what you've got to do.

I fold the sign and stuff it into the front of my coat. It's like my belly reads it 'cause it growls, extra long and loud.

"Shut up," I say, but it doesn't listen. Some of my body parts have minds of their own.

Stretching up to the Warrior Angel, I pat his feet goodbye and maybe for luck since Mr. Lincoln's broken. My fingers glide over the grapes and vines chiseled around his pedestal.

Even now, he doesn't give me a second look. I get that pretty much everywhere we go. My legs shake, still not sure about disobeying Mama, but a family of one isn't much of a family. The sun stretches more color across the sky now, kicking the morning in the butt with pinks, purples and oranges. Mama loves days like this. I hate that we're not watching it together.

Dang. O'Dell's tires squeal against the pavement up ahead and his truck's hauling this way. Here comes one of his drive-by ass chewings. He's just fifteen, but works full time and hassles us double time. He usually drives a white Eternal Peace pickup, but that's his truck since he's just getting to work. It's a total piece of crap and about the same color.

I stop in my tracks, remembering what O'Dell told Mama yesterday. "You two better leave today for good … or else."

Continue reading at https://marcymckay.com/books/.

Books from SkipJack Publishing

FICTION:

Marcy McKay

Pennies from Burger Heaven, by Marcy McKay

Stars Among the Dead, by Marcy McKay

The Moon Rises at Dawn, by Marcy McKay

Bones and Lies Between Us, by Marcy McKay

R.L. Nolen

Deadly Thyme, by R. L. Nolen

The Dry, by Rebecca Nolen

Ken Oder

The Closing, by Ken Oder

Old Wounds to the Heart, by Ken Oder

The Judas Murders, by Ken Oder

The Princess of Sugar Valley, by Ken Oder

Gay Yellen

The Body Business, by Gay Yellen

The Body Next Door, by Gay Yellen

Pamela Fagan Hutchins

THE *PATRICK FLINT* SERIES OF WYOMING MYSTERIES:

Switchback (Patrick Flint #1), by Pamela Fagan Hutchins

Snake Oil (Patrick Flint #2), by Pamela Fagan Hutchins

Sawbones (Patrick Flint #3), by Pamela Fagan Hutchins

Scapegoat (Patrick Flint #4), by Pamela Fagan Hutchins

Snaggle Tooth (Patrick Flint #5), by Pamela Fagan Hutchins

Stag Party (Patrick Flint #6), by Pamela Fagan Hutchins

Spark (Patrick Flint 1.5): Exclusive to subscribers, by Pamela Fagan Hutchins

THE *WHAT DOESN'T KILL YOU* SUPER SERIES:

Act One (WDKY Ensemble Prequel Novella): Exclusive to Subscribers, by Pamela Fagan Hutchins

The Essential Guide to the What Doesn't Kill You Series, by Pamela Fagan Hutchins

Katie Connell Caribbean Mysteries:

Saving Grace (Katie #1), by Pamela Fagan Hutchins

Leaving Annalise (Katie #2), by Pamela Fagan Hutchins

Finding Harmony (Katie #3), by Pamela Fagan Hutchins

Seeking Felicity (Katie #4), by Pamela Fagan Hutchins

Emily Bernal Texas-to-New Mexico Mysteries:

Heaven to Betsy (Emily #1), by Pamela Fagan Hutchins

Earth to Emily (Emily #2), by Pamela Fagan Hutchins

Hell to Pay (Emily #3), by Pamela Fagan Hutchins

Michele Lopez Hanson Texas Mysteries:

Going for Kona (Michele #1), by Pamela Fagan Hutchins

Fighting for Anna (Michele #2), by Pamela Fagan Hutchins

Searching for Dime Box (Michele #3), by Pamela Fagan Hutchins

Maggie Killian Texas-to-Wyoming Mysteries:

Buckle Bunny (Maggie Prequel Novella), by Pamela Fagan Hutchins

Shock Jock (Maggie Prequel Short Story), by Pamela Fagan Hutchins

Live Wire (Maggie #1), by Pamela Fagan Hutchins

Sick Puppy (Maggie #2), by Pamela Fagan Hutchins

Dead Pile (Maggie #3), by Pamela Fagan Hutchins

Ava Butler Caribbean Mysteries: A Sexy Spin-off From *What Doesn't Kill You*

Bombshell (Ava #1), by Pamela Fagan Hutchins

Stunner (Ava #2), by Pamela Fagan Hutchins

Knockout (Ava #3), by Pamela Fagan Hutchins

Poppy Needs a Puppy (Poppy & Petey #1), by Pamela Fagan Hutchins, illustrated by Laylie Frazier

MULTI-AUTHOR:

Murder, They Wrote: Four SkipJack Mysteries, by Ken Oder, R.L. Nolen, Marcy McKay, and Gay Yellen

Tides of Possibility, edited by K.J. Russell

Tides of Impossibility, edited by K.J. Russell and C. Stuart Hardwick

NONFICTION:

Marcy McKay

Transforming Your Stress (When Life Feels like a House Fire), by Marcy McKay

Helen Colin

My Dream of Freedom: From Holocaust to My Beloved America,

by Helen Colin

Pamela Fagan Hutchins

The Clark Kent Chronicles, by Pamela Fagan Hutchins

Hot Flashes and Half Ironmans, by Pamela Fagan Hutchins

How to Screw Up Your Kids, by Pamela Fagan Hutchins

How to Screw Up Your Marriage, by Pamela Fagan Hutchins

Puppalicious and Beyond, by Pamela Fagan Hutchins

What Kind of Loser Indie Publishes,and How Can I Be One, Too?, by Pamela Fagan Hutchins

Ken Oder

Keeping the Promise, by Ken Oder

Audio, e-book, and paperback versions of most titles available.

Made in the USA
Coppell, TX
10 March 2022

74787489R00144